(re)making a sandwich

an addiction case study

Mike Grant
LCSW, CADC II

Kelly

Keep running, and thanks
for the support to
keep helping our people!

Keep

ISBN: 978-0-5789-1352-0 (Paperback)
ISBN: 978-0-5789-1353-7 (E-Book)

Cover design by Charles Patterson

Interior design by Andy Meaden meadencreative.com

First edition 2021

Contact the author at: aidstationtherapy@gmail.com

Dedication

To Dana, Deacon, and Joseph.

Wherever the four of us may be, we will always be we.

CONTENTS

The Multnomah County Circuit Court in Portland, Oregon administers an innovative jail diversion program designed to reduce recidivism rates for habitual Driving Under the Influence (DUI) offenders. The initiative, called the Diversion Intensive Supervision Program (DISP), is a three-year program consisting of: three years of active supervision, which includes one year of substance abuse outpatient treatment with weekly group counseling and bi-weekly individual counseling; random urine drug screens (UDS) for the duration of the supervision; an alcohol monitoring leg bracelet for the first 90 days of the program; two community-based support groups per week (Alcoholics Anonymous, Narcotics Anonymous, SMART Recovery, etc.); monthly meetings with a DISP Case Manager; and on-time payment of restitution, supervision fees, and treatment fees, which can be substantial.

Clients who fulfill the above requirements will have the DUI charge erased from their records and all other DUI-related court-imposed sanctions lifted upon their completion of the program. Those who are not successful in completing the program for any reason, including an inability to pay all required fees, may be jailed for up to 12 months.

The following account is based on the true story of an actual DISP participant—herein called Frank—as seen through the lens of a fictional research study designed to assess the most effective elements of the diversion program. At intake, Frank was paired with a Primary

Counselor who administered screening and assessment questionnaires, the results of which provide additional background. Frank's story is told through a series of modified case notes that largely retain the stream-of-consciousness dialogue of the individual and group therapy sessions. Please note that the account contains certain fictional elements and all names have been changed to ensure confidentiality.

BACKGROUND

Frank is a 36-year-old Caucasian, cisgender, able-bodied, straight, self-identified male. He was born in the Upper Peninsula of Michigan on an Ojibwe Native American Reservation and states he has a small percentage of Native American heritage. He is also a veteran of the U.S. Army with an honorable discharge. Frank meets the diagnostic criteria for alcohol dependence and has a family history of alcohol abuse. His environment for most of his life has been intertwined with alcohol-related activities and relationships. Frank's physical health is beginning to deteriorate and his mental health has been negatively affected by the consequences of his inability to control his use. He also has significant motivation to make behavioral changes, including his desire to ameliorate the legal and health factors noted above and to provide his young child with a stable father. Frank is participating in this program after having been charged with his third DUI in 11 years.

5/8/12
Intake: Screening and Assessment

Screening:

Frank was screened using this series of questions from the DSM-IV's[1] evaluation of alcohol dependence. Comments are taken from his Primary Counselor's case notes.

1. **In the past year, have you had to drink much more than you once did to get the effect that you want, or found that your usual number of drinks had much less effect than before?**

   "Yes. I can drink a lot. I do get really drunk; the amount that I drink would get just about anybody wasted." Frank states that he drinks anywhere from two to 15 beers per session, and drinks four to five days per week.

2. **Did you have withdrawal symptoms and/or use alcohol to diminish withdrawal symptoms?**

   "Yes, and it sucks," Frank answers, "because I'm the worst parent during hangovers. I just turn on some cartoons and give my son some oatmeal and sleep until the next parenting responsibility pops up. It's not fair to him. My hangovers are horrible; I feel dead.

---

1 *Diagnostic and Statistical Manual of Mental Disorders, 4th Edition, Text Revision.* Washington, DC: APA, 2000

I lie around and sleep for hours, I call in sick to work, my stomach feels like a sewage pipe. If I really go at it, the next day I will have the shakes. Sometimes I'll drink in the morning, but that's usually just in the case of a sporting event and it's very seldom."

3. **Have you used alcohol in larger amounts or for longer periods than you intended?**

"Yeah; if I'm out with people, I don't have an 'off switch.' It takes something outside of myself to stop drinking." He notes that he starts most days intending not to drink, "but at some point, I start having thoughts about drinking just one or two, and I ultimately talk myself into buying a six-pack."

4. **Have you had a persistent desire, or made unsuccessful attempts, to cut down or control your use?**

"Definitely, yes. I tell myself all the time that I'm not going to drink today," Frank answers, "but it's a long day. And I always end up drinking. I've also tried to stop in the past because I recognized I wasn't doing anything productive with my life. I moved to Portland from Michigan and haven't really done anything exciting since I moved or taken advantage of the Pacific Northwest. Besides, I'm usually too messed up to remember what I have done."

5. **Have you spent a great deal of time obtaining the substance, using the substance, and/or recovering from the effects of the substance?**

"Yes, I've spent a lot of time using and recovering from alcohol," Frank admits, adding, "the recovering piece is getting harder and harder."

6. **Have you given up or reduced social, occupational, and/or recreational activities because of your substance use?**

"Absolutely yes; I've never been able to keep employment. I've had so many jobs and only two of those I didn't get fired and during both I was a mess. Over the last couple of years, I quit exercising. I used to play a lot of basketball and would go running but I never do either of those anymore. I've lost some friendships. When I got out of the Army at age 21, I moved up to East Lansing, Michigan, where some of my friends were attending Michigan State. I moved into their big college house with them. Most of those guys are still close to one another but I couldn't maintain those relationships; they all grew up while I was busy finding the next party."

7. **Have you continued to use alcohol despite knowledge of a persistent or recurrent physical or psychological problem that has likely been caused or exacerbated by the substance?**

"Yes. I can see the physical impact with the weight gain and COPD. I also still smoke cigarettes, which I know I need to quit. I also know I keep acting irresponsibly, which is stressful, and that cycle keeps me depressed. And when I'm forced to confront the

Background

financial messes from my behavior, I get anxious and have trouble sleeping."

(Answering "yes" to three or more of the DSM-IV's seven screening tool questions indicates a person meets the criteria for alcohol dependence. Frank answered yes to all seven.)

Assessment:

The questions below are from the American Society of Addiction Medicine[2] and are intended to elicit further information regarding the nature of the substance use.

1. **Acute Intoxication and/or Withdrawal Potential**:
   Frank states that he has not consumed any substances, aside from nicotine, in over three weeks. Frank denies a history of seizures or delirium tremens (DT) but clarifies that he's "had the shakes for ten years." Frank reports that alcohol is his drug of choice and he has had little experience with opioids or benzos. Frank shares that he has used the following substances at some point in his life: alcohol, nicotine, marijuana, cocaine, speed, heroin, ecstasy, LSD, mushrooms, and methadone.

---

2 Mee-Lee D, Shulman GD, Fishman MJ, Gastfriend DR, Miller, eds. *The ASAM Criteria: Treatment Criteria for Addictive, Substance-Related, and Co-Occurring Conditions. 3rd ed.* Carson City, NV: The Change Companies; 2013. Copyright 2013 by the American Society of Addiction Medicine.

2. **Biomedical Conditions and Complications:**

Frank states that he was diagnosed with Chronic Obstructive Pulmonary Disease (COPD) at age 33 but believes that he was misdiagnosed. "I rode a bike to my first check-up and was so out of shape that it sounded like I was dying," he explains. "It's pretty bad," he continues, laughing, "when that's what you're holding onto: that you're so out of shape that from riding a bike you sound like you have COPD." Frank acknowledges that he continues to smoke cigarettes, doesn't use his prescribed inhaler, does not exercise, and feels that he is about 40 pounds overweight; "I'm only 5'9" and I shouldn't be carrying over 200lbs!" He states that he often has difficulty falling asleep, which is typically due to stress over money and its multiple repercussions. "I burn up most of my energy at work and feel tired a lot when I'm home, which sucks," notes Frank, "because that's when I should be playing with my son."

3. **Emotional, Behavioral or Cognitive Conditions and Complications:**

Frank reports that he has had long periods of feeling depressed in the past, but concedes, "I have a hard time telling if it's depression or just the booze." He confides that he has, in the past, often had thoughts about suicide and occasionally still does. Frank states his suicidal ideation involves feeling that he's worthless, and that he hasn't done anything meaningful with his life." He also feels he's a burden to others and sees death as the only way to end that. He reports, "I have jumped in front of vehicles a couple times and bounced off the hood, and one time I tried to drink enough brandy to not wake up," but concedes, "If I really wanted to do it I could have come up with something better than that." Frank shares that the suicidal ideation/attempts all occurred before he had his son, and declares, "That kind of shit is no longer an option." He states that he cannot remember a time when he didn't engage in negative self-talk, stating "I did that before I started drinking—you can only imagine how bad the self-talk has gotten with the life I've made for myself." He also discusses symptoms of anxiety he's had for most of his adult life. Frank relates that he struggles with racing thoughts when he tries to fall asleep, describing those thoughts as often focusing on areas of his life he finds stressful or that feel out of his control. Frank has not accessed mental health treatment services in the past.

4. **Readiness to Change:**

    Frank states, "I continue to prove to myself that I can't control my alcohol use and now it no longer just hurts me, it affects my son as well." Frank shares that he would like to be able to "clean up" his legal issues, quit smoking, exercise more, and "figure out why I keep doing this to myself." Frank wants to quit drinking and says, "I'm tired of the bullshit that comes with booze." Frank completed an alcohol diversion program in 2009, which he dismisses as "a joke; I watched some Meg Ryan movie where she was a drunk and her husband stood by her or some shit, and then I went to the bar I worked at and got fucked up. I would have gotten more from watching Innerspace."

5. **Relapse, Continued Use, or Continued Problem Potential:**

Frank states that he once abstained from alcohol for three months, "but didn't do meetings or treatment, just used willpower." He shares that his triggers are typically his frustration around the financial cost of the program, anger that comes from his co-parenting relationship, and not knowing another way to live. Frank acknowledges he has been living by the mantra "It is what it is" for so long that he doesn't know how to change. He also engages in negative self-talk that undermines any desire he has to abstain, stating that it allows him to say, "fuck it," and go drink. Frank notes that his relationship with his son's mother ended a few months ago and that the stress of co-parenting will be difficult to manage without alcohol. He also reveals that he has been a "womanizer" for much of his adult life, and being single and alone may make him want to go to a bar and "pick someone up."

6. **Recovery/Living Environment:**

Frank shares that he has a four-year-old son, James, who is his primary motivator for recovery, although his relationship with James' mother will likely "always be a shit show." Frank is the assistant manager of a grocery store deli and notes that although he doesn't love the work, "it pays the bills," and his employer is working with him to meet the requirements of the program. Frank states that he doesn't know anyone who doesn't drink alcohol and most of his friendships are with people he has been drinking with for an extended period of time. Frank reports that he has two brothers and a sister who drink socially, but he doesn't feel that their use is problematic, and they don't use other drugs. Frank has distanced himself from his family over the years because he feels "It's better for them not to see me and worry," as he does not believe that he brings anything positive to their lives. Frank notes that his mom and stepdad have been drinking alcohol in excess since they started dating when he was five years old. He shares, "The drinking wasn't always the easiest thing to be around as the oldest child." When asked to clarify this statement, Frank explains, "As the oldest kid, you have to be the one to stop your parents' fights, and I had to do that a lot. I would wake up at night hearing the sound of our family's car door slamming, signaling that my parents were home from the bar. Once I knew our mom and stepdad were home, I always cautioned my siblings that no matter what they heard, they were not supposed to leave their rooms. I still get jumpy when I hear a car door slamming loudly late at night." Frank discloses that while he has been going to Alcoholics Anonymous (AA) meetings, he struggles to make connections with people.

After completion of the assessment, Frank and the Primary Counselor develop a treatment plan designed to help Frank meet his objectives.

TREATMENT PLAN

Problems (direct client quotes):

1. Got to stop drinking
2. Would like to quit smoking
3. Need to get back in shape
4. Would like to quit beating myself up with negative self-talk

Strengths:

1. Don't want my son following my alcohol abuse path
2. Hard worker
3. Funny and make friends easily
4. Tired of living this way

Objectives:

1. To learn strategies to maintain abstinence from alcohol and nicotine.

2. To learn coping skills to manage challenging emotions and maladaptive thinking.

3. To develop an exercise routine to help with health concerns.

4. To learn about shame and the connection it has to alcohol abuse.

Treatment Interventions:

1. Weekly group sessions. Homework will be completed in its entirety and ready to present to other group members at each group session.

2. Individual sessions with primary counselor every two weeks.

3. Homework topics to include alcohol and drug psychoeducation, coping skills, thinking errors, shame, smoking cessation resources, and exercise planning.

4. Random UDS to monitor abstinence.

5. Primary Counselor will utilize Motivational Interviewing, Cognitive Behavioral Therapy, and Narrative Therapy Evidence-Based Therapies.

TREATMENT

5/24/2012
Individual Session: 60 Minutes

Frank arrives at his first individual session with his Primary Counselor on time. He shares that navigating the public transportation system from his work to treatment was difficult and he'll need to adjust his schedule, stating, "It's definitely way harder when you don't have a car—I end up leaving really early because I'm afraid of being late, but that extra time cuts into my work hours even more. I end up here early, with nothing to do, spending time waiting for therapy instead of working or spending time with my son. But I know I won't get any slack if I'm late, and I don't want to end up in front of the judge just because I missed a bus connection or something like that!"

Frank's last reported use of alcohol and marijuana was on 4/13/2012. He relates that the judge who oversees the DISP program told him that if he continued to use substances, he would not be allowed to enter the program. He reports that he went to a bar with a couple of his oldest friends, people he went to high school with in Michigan, and told them that this would be the last time he would be drinking for at least three years. Frank shares that they knew about the DUI and that he was going to have consequences, but "they didn't know I would have to quit for real." Frank shares his impression that they seemed supportive, but they were aware this was going to change their relationships with him.

Frank reports that he "got wasted and felt like crap the next day," and has not had a drink since that date. He notes that "it's been nice not to have any hangovers," and says he found several Alcoholics Anonymous (AA) groups that he can attend when his son is with his [son's] mother, sharing, "I can see why people dig it. It's cool to hear that people are as messed up as you."

Frank admits he struggles with "the God connection to AA, even though I've heard people say, 'God can be whatever you want it to be.' If it's whatever I want it to be, then why is it included? People feel strongly about their own beliefs and experiences about God and religion, which I'd guess is why the concept is included in the program. Given that, I'm confused by the idea of using the term 'God' to refer to whatever you want. But if it's helping people not screw up their lives, then, shit, let God be a cloud, doorknob, or divine being. Who am I to judge?"

When Frank is asked at what points during his life his

drinking has been most extreme, he references the three-year period he was in the U.S. Army. He relates that he enlisted at age eighteen, went to boot camp in Kentucky, and then was stationed in Germany for most of the remainder of his service. He explains that his time in Germany occurred during the Clinton Administration, and that certain policy changes made shortly before his enlistment greatly affected his experience. One initiative, called Single Soldier Quality of Life (SSQL), extended to single soldiers on base the same freedoms enjoyed by married soldiers living off base. "Some of these freedoms included fewer room inspections, allowing us to decorate our own barracks rooms as we saw fit, and the freedom to drink and have women stay in our rooms.

"We called President Clinton 'B-Funk,' Frank continues, "got to love B-Funk!" adding, "You had a bunch of young guys in a country where you could drink at age 18, no parents, and no inspections. It was a mess. Also, B-Funk wasn't getting us into a war, so we were on base and training during the day but had our nights free to let loose." He relates, in addition, that at the time he was engaged to marry his high school girlfriend, but, "she made a great move and called it off. We were young, and she could tell I was drinking a lot and couldn't even be sober for our scheduled phone calls."

Frank reveals that when the engagement ended, he started using other drugs as well, "because that's what my friends were doing. I had been saying no, but the breakup was all the permission I needed." He started with cannabis, then escalated to ecstasy and speed. "I lived in this huge room called *The Hanger* that had people partying in it all day and night. Drinking was a huge part of those days, but alcohol was still overshadowed by other drugs. At one point we were selling drugs and had this silver briefcase with all kinds of speed, ecstasy, and weed in it, plus names of people who owed money. If that suitcase had ever been found, we would all have been fucked. We had a room inspection one time, and we had the briefcase hidden under the garbage can. I was absolutely freaking out, but the inspection team didn't find it. We hid other paraphernalia up in the rafters of a meeting room to which we had access. I was sent to Bosnia on a NATO peace-keeping mission for six of the last eight months I was enlisted, which in retrospect I believe probably saved me from serious legal trouble in the Army. When I went back to Germany after Bosnia, I immediately fell right back into my heavy drinking."

Frank shares that in 2002, he and his then-girlfriend moved from Michigan to Portland, Oregon. He recalls, "It was fun when we got here. We had some stress prior to leaving Michigan but the move united us, and we were excited to give a new town a shot. We moved in with my best friend and his girlfriend who had relocated here the year prior. We had a great time at the start, and I got a job pretty quickly in a grocery store. We eventually felt secure enough to get our own place, and that's about the time it started to unravel. Once again, a woman made a smart move and left me. Looking back, had my addiction at that time not been out of control, I think we could have had a good life, but I was drinking all the time and fucked it up. In my mind, her departure gave me a green light to go crazy in a new town."

He relates that about a year and a half after this split, he started working as a bartender at a dive bar that had live music, "mostly punk and metal," and ended up working there for the next seven years. "The only reason I was able to keep that job was because I could drink while I was working." Frank explains that he drank a lot during the first six years of bartending, as well as using cocaine on a regular basis. "I loved being a bartender at that bar," he recalls. "It was the type of place where you could sit next to someone who was completely different from you and have a great night. It was a very eclectic group of people, very blue collar, lots of service industry folks. Fun and good natured, non-judgmental. There were people from all kinds of backgrounds, and it gave me a chance to see things from so many different points of view. Most of the people I'm currently connected to in this town were connected to that bar in some way. It was rough, and my body paid the price, but it was worth it.

"Even though most of the people I knew during that time were going at it hard, they didn't seem to get as messed up as I did. At some point during a binge, they would think about the fact that they had something to do in the morning and stop using and act in a responsible manner. The next day hardly concerned me, which it should have because I was usually worthless after a bender." He adds, "I put myself in so many bad spots, it could easily have killed me."

When asked about the DUI that brought him to treatment, Frank begins by describing the split between him and his son's mother in late January 2012. "It sucked, but we were toxic for each other and it would've gotten worse. It wasn't bad at the start. Having a kid together, while challenging, is magical. The 'honeymoon' period after the birth has a way of showcasing your finer qualities and hiding your faults...until it doesn't any longer. It got to a point where we couldn't fake being happy."

He relates that he had grown accustomed to their life together in the large house they shared. After the split, he would go home and the silence in that big, empty space would feel overwhelmingly lonely.

Frank recounts the night of the DUI, describing his plans to meet friends that evening and the fact that he had gone home after work to get ready. All day he'd told himself that he would use public transportation instead of driving his "50-cc moped that I take to work." Frank explains that he talked himself into driving because "I didn't want to miss any of the NBA Slam Dunk Contest; to this day I have no idea who was in that contest. Even though I had to work the next morning at 7:00 a.m. and I had the moped, I started drinking and didn't stop. I snuck away from people and drove home in a blackout and ran into a parked van nowhere near my house. The police officer asked me why I was driving the moped and I told him I wasn't driving it and that he had the wrong guy. The police officer reminded me that I was still wearing the helmet, which I told him was for safety! I broke my clavicle and blew a .21 on the breathalyzer test.

"I had no business driving. I could have severely hurt someone else or myself. My son would've had to tell people that his dad died on a moped while driving drunk, which is just fucking stupid." Frank estimates that he drank and drove "thousands of times," frequently in a blackout, and states that he once damaged the side of his truck by veering into a concrete barrier while exiting a highway—a truck he later wrecked entirely during one of these blackouts. "And that's just the stuff I can remember," he adds. Frank concedes that over the years, countless friends tried to stop him from driving while under the influence by offering to pay for a cab, drive him home, or let him sleep it off on their couches. "I never listened and sometimes I would get mad and try to fight them…that's how fucked my brain is. I don't even know how to describe it; it's reasoning with the unreasonable!"

Frank continues, "My best friend bailed me out the morning of this last DUI. He's actually bailed me out of jail many times. You know you got both problems and a pretty good friend when the same person has bailed you out of jail several times in a number of different states. I used to go to jail so often in East Lansing, Michigan that I would call him but have him wait to come get me until after breakfast, which the jail contracted with McDonald's for—might as well get a McMuffin out of it," Frank laughs. "I've done a little time in every town I've spent time in. Anyway, we had breakfast and he told me that I had to stay away from vehicles. I replied that it wasn't the vehicles that were the problem..."

Primary Counselor probes slightly, asking Frank what he meant by that statement and how he felt when he said it.

"That was the first real moment when I recognized that I can't drink anymore," Frank replies, "and that I will never move forward in my life if I keep drinking. I was tired of putting myself in those positions. I felt exhausted and just really mad at myself."

Frank starts crying and does not speak for a while. When he does, he says, "I don't need any more reasons to be pissed off about my life.

Frank pauses for breath and then shakes his head, "I understand that I'm a fuck-up, but to start fucking up my kid's life is agonizing. I'm going to have to spend so much money and energy to fix this, and who knows when I will drive again. James will be riding public transportation with me for the next three years, minimum, plus I will have no money this summer. I don't know how we'll do it. He doesn't deserve this shit."

Primary Counselor asks Frank what he does when he's feeling overwhelmed by the responsibilities he has in his life.

"Ha!" Frank responds, "I think you mean besides drink? Well, I just started running and it's been helping. I got this running stroller off Craigslist for like $25 and I run my son to the park where he can play. The park is close which is lucky because I can't run very far but it helps me chill out and it can't hurt my efforts to drop some of this weight, plus James loves it." Asked how he feels now when thinking about the time at the park with his son compared to a few minutes ago, Frank reflects, "I feel better. I get so worked up thinking about the money and the future, but my kid only cares about hanging out and having fun. He's just a kid who can have fun doing just about anything. There's this rap group called Jurassic 5 and they have this line that says, 'the most you can spend on a child is time' and that's what James needs. I don't think I ever would've even considered quitting if it weren't for him. He's the first thing in my life that has allowed me to get out of my own screwed up head and think about someone else. I know I didn't stop drinking until now, but I had made some changes in my life to try to be a somewhat good dad, and that's because he deserves a chance. I don't want him to have to live this way anymore; it's fucking exhausting for both of us."

Primary Counselor asks Frank to complete the Michigan Alcohol Screening Test (MAST) to help him evaluate his alcohol problem level and then to present it in his first group counseling session which is scheduled two weeks hence. Frank confirms that he understands the expectations, remarking, "A screening tool from Michigan—seems fitting."

6/6/2012
Group Counseling Session: 90 minutes

Group format consists of each participant's check–in at the beginning of group, presentation of homework, group conversation over homework and any weekly events any client wants to discuss. To check in, each client shares his/her date of last use of a substance, mood on a one-through-ten scale with ten being the best, any recent urges and/or triggers to use, commitment to remaining abstinent, and whether they has homework to present.

Eleven members are present for group. The group consists of people in three phases of treatment. Those in Phase Three have been in treatment the longest and are closest to finishing the year-long group therapy commitment. Frank checks into group, stating his clean date is 4/14/2012. He shares his mood is a seven, explaining, "I'm glad I was able to get to group on time and I've had a pretty good week," although he acknowledges that he has recently had some urges to drink as a result of disagreements with the mother of his son, and that he "really just wanted to get messed up." He estimates his commitment to staying sober as about 80 percent, because "I have to take care of this legal mess and I've been trying to go around it for years. I know I have to go through it now, but still not sure if I can." Frank affirms that he has homework ready to present.

During check-in, a peer named Tom shares about a recent relapse and its consequences. He reports that he was sanctioned with a probation violation (PV) and he went to jail for three days. Tom states that he "came up hot for opiates from pills from an old prescription," saying "I had some serious tooth pain, so I took medication. What was I supposed to do, be in pain? The problem with this program is they don't give a shit if you're in pain, they got no compassion. I mean look at this place! If they cared about us at all we wouldn't be sitting in a circle on these hard metal chairs with the seat padding squashed flat as a pancake!" Tom exhales audibly before adding, "As long as they get theirs."

The peer who's been in group the longest, Randy, raises his hand to give feedback. "It sucks you were in pain, man; I know how that is, you can't think of anything else, it kills. But I think you did have other options. You know how this works; you must go to them before they come to you. How do they know you used prescription pills and not heroin? You didn't give them an option. What are they supposed to do, trust you? We're a group of untrustworthy motherfuckers, man! You let it show up on a test without calling your counselor and telling her your story—their hands were tied. Like I said, it sucks for you to have all that going on, but we got new guys in here that need to know there are ways to do this right and ways that will put you in jail for a weekend."

After check-in, Primary Counselor asks Frank to share his homework. Frank responds that he completed the MAST, a screening tool to gauge his alcohol problem level. Then she inquires what Frank learned from this assignment, at which point Frank laughs and responds, "that I have some issues." Frank informs the group that the MAST is made up of 25 yes or no questions, and you get a certain number of points—the number of points varies among the questions—depending on your answer. He explains the scoring: "Zero to three total points means you have no apparent problem, four points equals an early or middle problem drinker, and five points or more equates to a problem drinker or an alcoholic." Frank relates that his score was a "44!" and that "it was like the universe was trying to hit me in the head with a hammer to make it clear. I knew I had a problem, but that's a pretty big score. And my past arrests and DUIs pumped up the score." When asked his takeaway from the assignment, Frank replies "I needed the results to be this clear so I can't start telling myself that maybe I don't have a problem or it's just some bad luck. There is no wiggle room on this; I'm a drunk. I guess my only justification would be that it seems that most people I know would score higher than a five; most people have felt guilty about their drinking or had someone complain—shit that's four points right there."

The group is asked if Frank's logic is flawed. They remain silent briefly and then a Phase Three peer named Caesar replies, "Drinkers hang out with drinkers, and there are a bunch of people who don't drink like us. Just because all the people you know drink a lot doesn't mean the people who aren't hanging out in dive bars drink every day."

Primary Counselor shares that research supports this statement, suggesting that the top ten percent of drinkers consume over 50 percent of all the alcohol dispensed. In other words, one out of ten drinkers imbibes over ten drinks per day. Research also shows that approximately 25 percent of people in the United States don't drink at all and the average consumption of people who do drink alcohol is three drinks per week. Frank reflects on these figures and comments, "So what you're saying is that if the 11 of us were in that top ten percent, together we would have consumed in total around 110 drinks today? And even if we were all having off days and drank half that, we would be putting down 55 drinks? No wonder we all have multiple DUI's!"

An older woman named Sharon shares, "I wouldn't be drinking that many; I would only have a few glasses of wine after work." A younger peer quickly interjects, "If Sharon isn't going to drink those other seven glasses, I call dibs!"

6/12/2012
Individual Session: 60 Minutes

Frank shows up on time for this session. He looks slightly unkempt; his beard is longer and his clothes are untidy, which contrasts with his normal clean-cut presentation. When asked how he's feeling, Frank replies, "I'm pretty stressed out; the cost of this program is too much. I had group last week and group this week, this session, and two UDS tests; that's $170 in one week[3]. I work in a grocery store making sandwiches, and this shit isn't calculus; it's simple math and it don't add up. I don't know how people are expected to do it."[4]

My case manager told me, "you always found a way to pay for your alcohol," which is some insensitive bullshit and really shows how we are all viewed. You don't know how I drank! Yes, occasionally, I would go out and spend some real money, but most of the time I drank at a friend's bar, so I would get hooked up. Nine out of ten times I would drink a six pack at home, which cost five dollars. I have a kid; I can't spend money like that on booze."

Primary Counselor reflects back to Frank that she hears that he is experiencing frustration and finding the experience really challenging.

---

3 The client must pay all fees associated with UDS, group, and individual counseling at the time each is incurred. For the first 90 days, Frank must pay the clinic either $105 or $145 weekly, depending on the number of UDS he's assigned.
4 Oregon's minimum wage in 2012 was $8.80/hour; $352 per 40-hour week.

"It's super frustrating, I don't know if I'm going to be able to do this," Frank responds. "I had to sell plasma twice this week just to have money to pay for these appointments. I never sold plasma for alcohol; even booze didn't drive me to do that."

Primary Counselor said, "I can see that's not what you want to do, but it's showing how resourceful you are. It might not be what you want to hear, but you're actively problem solving, Primary Counselor observes. What was your method for problem solving in the past?"

Frank replies dismissively, "This isn't nothing new for me, I know how to be poor. I know how to grind through life and make shit harder than it has to be. That's my skillset, just getting by. That shit should be on my tombstone."

Primary Counselor follows up, "What's the difference between now and times in the past when you were just getting by, besides the significant challenge of the cost of this program?" Frank thinks for a few moments and shares "I haven't had booze in almost two months. I have to sit with everything that's happening in my life because I don't get to drink it into tomorrow. I can't use alcohol to postpone my awareness of reality, or the need to deal with it, which I have to say pisses me off a lot of the time. If I were still drinking, I wouldn't be in this program. I wouldn't be paying any of these fees. I would have avoided taking responsibility for my actions. I would have just said 'fuck it' and left it to Multnomah County to find and arrest me. Obviously, that scenario would be disastrous long-term, but in a weird way, waiting to be arrested would entail a lot fewer responsibilities day-to-day."

Primary Counselor asks about the stress, frustration and financial insecurity Frank's experiencing, and what methods he's using to cope with it.

"My roommate gave me some great advice when I started this," Frank replies. "He said, 'whenever you want a drink, just go for a run.' He runs marathons and told me it helps him manage all the stress in his life. I've always enjoyed running but you can't be an alcoholic like me and run, so I'd run once, then not again for weeks or months. That's not running. I told you I've been running with my son in his stroller. We're going to parks now that are farther out than those we went to in the past, which is cool for me—I can see that the exercise is working. I'm nowhere near being what I consider a runner, but I run a few miles three or four times per week. The other day, James was with his mom and she called and we got into some stupid argument over nothing. I told her I had to go. I put the phone down and ran right out of the house. I was still wearing my work clothes, although thankfully I already had on running shoes, and I just took off; ran three miles, came back and that tension I had in my neck and the desire to get drunk was gone. I actually felt pretty good."

Primary Counselor enthuses, "It's great that you were able to notice the fact that using a coping skill like running can reduce your stress level and allow you to navigate through a craving like that. How would you have handled that, say, three months ago?"

"I would have gotten drunk, without a doubt," Frank responds immediately.

"What else are you doing to help yourself cope? It would be great if you could use running every time, but you can't. If you happened to get upset by something we were discussing, for instance, you couldn't just run out of here because there would be consequences, so what are you doing in those kinds of moments?"

Frank is laughing loudly when he replies, "Sorry, but I'm just imagining what it would look like if I ran out of here; having to tell my case manager, 'No you don't understand, I was coping!' I don't know, I'm just trying to take care of things as they come. I made this mess, so I got to clean it up. I mean, maybe it's unfortunate that alcoholism runs in my family, but where is crying about that going to get me? I'm tired of taking two steps back for every one step forward in my life; it looks stupid to walk the opposite direction of everyone else. If I start to feel sorry for myself or blame anyone but myself then I'm closer to messing this up."

Primary Counselor responds, "That's a very mature statement—you're holding yourself accountable for your own behavior. Do you think that way of thinking aligns more with the past, present, or future?"

Frank answers, "I can't stay in the past. I blame shit all the time on the past and all that's giving me is more things to blame. I think taking care of the problem in front of me keeps me in the present. I don't think I've thought about how much I blame the past and freak out about the future, and by freak out, I don't mean to the point of doing shit about it, just enough to ensure that I'm always a little miserable. Up until now I've avoided the present because it was cluttered with my mess and it's felt daunting to have to fix my life."

Primary Counselor asks, "Do you feel as though today you made progress on fixing your life?"

Frank reflects for a moment and replies, "I'm here, I have a little less plasma, a lot less money, but I didn't make my life worse today, and I for sure didn't make my son's life any worse today, so there's that."

Primary Counselor gives Frank a packet holding an assignment and a handout on Cognitive Distortions. Frank is told to follow the directions of the assignment and to present it at the group counseling session in two weeks.

6/20/2012
Group Counseling Session: 90 minutes

Ten members present for group. Frank checks into group stating his clean date remains 4/14/2012, but he classifies his mood as a five, noting that he is, "pretty stressed out about money." Frank admits that he had some urges recently when friends posted pictures from a camping trip, an event that he likely would have attended in the past, and it made him think about drinking with friends. Frank states that his commitment to staying sober is 70 percent, not more because "the money part is killing me." He also shares that he just reached 60 days clean and that this feels "pretty cool," and he wants to see what 90 days feels like. Frank states that he has his homework ready to present.

A new peer introduces himself as "John," and checks in. John states that his clean date is 5/25/2012 and alcohol is his drug of choice. John notes his mood is around a five; he's trying to stay positive but has some difficult things going on in his personal life. He often thinks about drinking to deal with stress but has not used, and his commitment to staying sober is "around 90 percent today but it fluctuates." John does not have homework to present.

Tom, who Frank learned at the first group is in trouble for using prescription opioids, is asked by Primary Counselor if he has anything to share. Tom sighs dramatically and exclaims, "If I must. I missed my UDS this past Monday. I called the damn phone line and I'm sure it said the color was brown. My color is blue so I didn't come in. My case manager called me at home and told me that I missed the UDS and that I had to give one that day and that the consequence of failing to show up that day would be another PV. I did it, but then got a call today from my Primary Counselor and case manager saying that the make-up UDS was positive for alcohol. I don't know where that came from. I haven't been drinking; you'd know if I'd been drinking, I can't hide if from people. I asked them to retest it. I don't know what the hell is going on around here. It would seem with all the damn money you're making you would have this working right! It's not like you're spending it on the fancy décor—fake plants and cheap motivational posters that look like they've been here since the 1980s! We can't even get a cup of coffee around here!"

Primary Counselor asks the group if anyone has feedback.

Frank raises his hand and says, "The only thing I can help with is that I have blue as my color and it was blue on Monday because I had to give a UDS that day; it may have been brown on Friday."

Sharon muses, "It was brown on Friday, you must have gotten your days mixed up."

"I didn't get my days mixed up!" Tom shouts.

Caesar quickly raises his hand and interjects, "Hey,

man, you don't need to be yelling, she was just trying to help."

"I don't recall asking for help," Tom replies, to which Caesar quickly responds, "You either need some help or you got some bad luck, my friend." Primary Counselor asks Caesar what he means by his last statement.

"I'm not trying to mess with you," Caesar assures Tom, "but one person said the color was blue on Monday, the other said it was brown on Friday. We've all messed up the colors, but you don't want to believe that you made that mistake. Then you tested positive for alcohol and don't know how that happened. If it's true, that's some bad luck, but your case manager isn't going to believe that, so you better figure out something else, that's all I'm saying."

Primary Counselor asks Tom how it feels to hear that from Caesar, to which Tom replies belligerently, "I don't care what he thinks about it, I know the truth and the…" Primary Counselor interrupts, "Tom, that's not the question I asked you. I asked how it feels to hear that?"

"I'm pretty pissed off," Tom mutters.

"Have there been times in your life when you have felt similarly—pissed off or upset—and it led to some thinking that in hindsight may have been unhealthy and led to negative consequences?" Primary Counselor asks. Tom begins to respond angrily and Primary Counselor again redirects him, saying, "We get it. You're upset and you see things differently, and that's ok. What I'm wondering is if you've had times when you were so mad that your thinking—the thoughts that were racing through your head—might have been unhealthy or not helpful to you? Go ahead and think about it for a few minutes and while you're thinking we'll continue group and come back to you. Does that sound alright?"

"Yeah, please move on," mumbles Tom.

After check-in, Primary Counselor asks Frank to present his homework. Frank says that he has completed the Cognitive Distortions packet.

"The stinking thinking packet—I did that one, it's good," Randy offers.

"I didn't know that's what they call it," Frank responds with some amusement.

"Yeah, that's what they call it in AA."

"Ok, well," Frank continues, "I was supposed to go through this packet and pick out the five Cognitive Distortions I engage in most and then give examples of each. I had to do five examples of each, but I only need to present one to the group." Primary Counselor interrupts to ask him to tell the group what Cognitive Distortions are.

"What I gathered is that these are thoughts that are irrational and that we frequently use to justify doing things that aren't good for us. And since we do this often, it becomes a regular practice. Everyone does it in some way, but we use those kinds of thoughts a lot to let us drink, use, cheat—all the negative stuff we do," Frank explains.

Primary Counselor adds, "It's also called maladaptive thinking, which means the thought is false or rationally unsupported, which can lead to unhealthy behaviors."

"I've used the following five Cognitive Distortions the most," Frank continues, "which I didn't even know was something I did prior to this assignment. The first is Minimization. This is something I did all the time, saying things like 'I'll just have a couple of beers, it's no big deal.' I hardly ever have 'just a couple,' especially if I'm going out to drink. The next one is Lying. I've lied a lot about my drinking, especially in my romantic relationships and with employers. I really hate that I did it, but that didn't stop me from doing it. I think I also lied to myself, or at least tried to. I didn't know that Shame thinking was a Cognitive Distortion, but I had Shame thoughts all the time, which almost always made me want to drink. I have beaten myself up and haven't liked myself in years. I have good friends, but I've often thought that if they knew what a piece of shit I am, they would never hang out with me. I also thought 'I deserve shitty things to happen to me because I'm not worth having good things happen to.' Another Cognitive Distortion I have used is playing the Victim. I did this when I was really stressed or mad, and I blamed other people when something was my fault. I blamed my childhood for years, which doesn't make sense because I'm the one who drove cars drunk, broke the laws, and sat in bars drinking until I blacked out; that was on me. Lastly, I have used Closed Thinking where I didn't listen to anyone because I either didn't want to hear it or because I thought I was right or smarter than others. If I didn't respond or listen, then I could avoid hearing about my drinking. I don't know how you become someone who thinks they are a piece of shit and at the same time thinks they are smarter than other people. That's crazy, right?"

Primary Counselor asks if others have similar stories around this kind of thinking. Several peers acknowledge that they can relate.

Randy confesses, "I would Minimize the impact my drinking and my behaviors had on people and say things like 'I'm doing them a favor by staying away so they don't have to worry.' But they did worry, and worried even more that I wasn't talking to them, but I didn't care because I was only thinking about me."

Sharon speaks up, "Wasn't sure if it was the Closed Thinking one but I would get mad and then not want to talk to my husband and would use it as an excuse to go to the tavern. I wouldn't be mad when I got home but my husband was!"

Laughing at Sharon's comment, Caesar chimes in, "I can relate to the Shame. My life's goal has always been to be different from my dad. He was an alcoholic and a deadbeat, in and out of our lives. I heard once that the things you're trying hardest to run from are the things you'll end up running toward. Well, in my case, that's true. I've spent years away from my kids. Always with an excuse to present to others, to appear to be someone different than who I am, but inside, the Shame was messing me up. I like that saying, 'If you talked to your friends like you talk to yourself, you wouldn't have any friends.' When I think of myself as a father, I just unload this negative tirade internally that sends me flying to alcohol, which hasn't helped anything."

Primary Counselor asks Tom if he notices any connection to any of these Cognitive Distortions, eliciting only a sigh—and the dismissive comment, "I don't, and I'm not really in a mood to talk about it."

"Well, that's definitely Closed Thinking," Sharon observes quietly.

7/3/2012
Individual Session: 60 Minutes

Frank arrives on time to his scheduled session. He is visibly upset, as evidenced by his facial expressions and body language. In response to Primary Counselor's question regarding his obvious distress, Frank replies, "This whole thing is pissing me off. I'm so mad right now. I had a UDS on Friday that I didn't have the money for, and I explained that I did not have the money and there was nothing I could do about it. I took a damn bus all the way across the city and I was told I couldn't take the UDS. Then I get a call from my case manager Monday saying I have a positive UDS—I don't know much about science, but I'm pretty sure you need some piss if you're going to claim it tested positive for substances. But that's the policy—if you can't pay it's counted as positive, so now I have a court date…which is time off work, which is less money to pay this. Am I crazy or does it feel like we're being set up to fail? Coming in here multiple times a week, waiting outside that locked door like a cow waiting to be let into the barn from the cold, finally being allowed in and then having to pay all that money to piss with somebody watching over my shoulder, and I'm scared I haven't drunk enough water to even be able to, but if I drink enough beforehand to piss, then I'm scared I won't be able to hold it 'til you guys finally let me in . . . This shit is a racket and the only things I'm getting from this are broke and mad!"

Primary Counselor lets Frank finish venting, then responds, "I can see that you're upset about the policies of the program you're in, and that the financial cost is really challenging for you." "This isn't challenging for me," Frank declares, "typing is challenging for me. This is impossible—I'm delaying a jail sentence and I might as well get it over with."

Primary Counselor reflects, "It sounds overwhelming, and I don't want to discount how tough this is, but can I ask a question about something you shared earlier?"

"Do what you got to do," Frank replies dismissively.

"You have, what, about 80 days clean or something like that?"

"Seventy-nine days; 11 until I get my 90-day chip."

Primary Counselor declares enthusiastically, "Great! 79 days and close to getting your chip. Besides that chip, can you name some things that you have gained from 79 days of being sober? It can be small, it doesn't matter, just anything that comes to mind."

Frank tussles with the question but after a few seconds responds consideringly, "Well, I haven't been sober this many days in a row since boot camp in 1994."

Primary Counselor's enthusiasm continues, "Okay, that's great! Through hard work, and despite challenging conditions, you've been sober for the longest time in almost twenty years, and that seems like a huge accomplishment."

Frank, his anger dissipating, concedes. "It feels good. I think with that and the running I can tell that I'm healthier. I've lost ten pounds—and I ran six miles the other day, which is the farthest I've ever gone!"

"On a one-to-ten scale, with ten being the most likely, how likely is it that, without treatment and abstinence, you would have lost ten pounds and run six miles?" asks Primary Counselor.

Frank chuckles, "C'mon, you know that wouldn't have happened, that would be lower than a one on the scale."

"Anything else you can think of?" Primary Counselor queries.

Frank ponders the question, then shares, "I'm having a nice time with James right now. We're broke, but we're making it work. We've been going to parks a lot and trying to do all the free movies and concerts the park offers. I have this alcohol monitoring bracelet that I can't submerge in water so we can't go swimming, but I've been running to different fountains in town and letting him play in the water. I get embarrassed about the bracelet, but my kid doesn't give a shit, and he's happy, so I got to get over that. It's just some stupid pride stuff; I'm ashamed now of the consequences of my behaviors but fear of future shame didn't stop me then from behaving in a way that produced these consequences."

Primary Counselor probes again, "Anything else?"

"I've been pretty solid at work lately, and not being hungover helps. Which is another thing; it's a big change not to have been hungover for this long. It allows me to work with my team with a little less frustration. I've still missed some work because of court dates and my kid getting sick, but I think I've been more dependable. It got me thinking: If I'm going to be sober, do I want to keep working in the grocery store deli? I don't know and I got no other skills; moving up in the company I work for will allow me to make the most money that I can."

"You've shared a lot and I want to make sure I'm getting everything, so would it be ok if I summarize what you've just shared?" Primary Counselor asks.

Frank nods.

"So, you've been clean and sober from all substances longer than you have in almost twenty years, and you've been running a lot and recently have felt accomplished about running six miles, the longest distance you've run since you started running again when you got sober. Those two things are helping you feel healthier and have resulted in a ten-pound weight loss. You've been more dependable at work, have less frustration with coworkers, and lastly, but it sounds like most importantly, you are enjoying time with your son, participating in lots of positive activities like going to the park, watching movies, and going to the water fountains. You acknowledge you feel some embarrassment about not being able to go swimming together, but you are setting that aside because what you're doing is making James happy. Did I get everything? Or did I misspeak at all?"

Frank, kind of laughing and smiling, says, "I think you got everything."

"Some of those are the goals that you outlined in your treatment plan a few months ago."

Frank nods in acknowledgment.

Primary Counselor continues, "Well, we have something dialectical happening, then. We have two seemingly opposing truths happening at the same time. Do you know what those two things are?

"Umm, well, I'm meeting some of my goals which feels pretty good, and umm, I'm not sure I'm getting the second."

"What did you share when you first came in today?" asks Primary Counselor.

"When I was mad, I was saying how hard this is and that I thought it was a racket."

"That's right," Primary Counselor nods, "the seemingly opposing realities are that you're meeting your goals, and yet, simultaneously, this work is really hard; on the one hand, you have a sense of being overwhelmed and powerless, and on the other, the evidence that you are making significant progress in undeniable. These are two things that appear contradictory but that are, in fact, happening concurrently. Life can be this way.

There's no doubt that going through this program while being a single parent is hard, and we have never told you otherwise. The good news is that you've been told how this program works, and in a few months, you will have fewer urine drug screens; you're a few weeks away from having the leg bracelet off; and you'll be done with groups in less than ten months. And all that will be a result of how hard you have worked to earn it. The only other question I have for you is whether all the positive things that have happened in the last 79 days are worth the challenges you're facing. I don't want an answer now, I just want you to think about it and answer when we meet again."

For group, Frank is assigned to write a Narrative Therapy paper externalizing his relationship with alcohol. Frank is given a handout outlining the expectations of the assignment and will be asked to share his assignment with the group in the next few weeks.

7/18/2012
Group Counseling: 90 Minutes

Eleven members present for group. Frank checks into group, stating that his clean date remains 4/14/2012. Frank classifies his mood as an eight out of ten because he's earned his 90-day chip. His comment elicits a round of applause. He relates that he's had few urges to use and his commitment to staying sober is 80 percent, as he's feeling "real motivated right now but broke as shit." Frank states that he has his homework ready to present.

John shares that his mood is around a four, but he doesn't have any urges to drink and "does not want to talk about it."

Sharon checks in, saying, "Things are going ok," then discloses that she's recently had a death in her family and that most of her family's mourning involves alcohol. "Since I knew it would be an Irish wake, I asked a cousin who's been clean forever to attend and to stick by me for support. It was good to have her there."

Tom checks in, reporting that he's "kind of upset," and when asked if he wants to reveal why, he states, "The last couple of groups I hadn't wanted to discuss what was going on with me, but I was pushed to share anyway. Then the group had to have a long talk about my situation, and it seemed that, despite knowing nothing about me, my life or my situation, everyone had an opinion they felt they needed to express. Now, however—

and I'm sorry John, just using you as an example—now when John states he doesn't want to share, no one says anything; it seems hypocritical."

John immediately speaks up, "Man, I have an 18-month-old son who's dying from a rare blood disease. I'm separated from his mom and she's keeping me away from my child for her own reasons, feels like spite. She has lots of money, good lawyers, and a mom who has mental health issues who wants to control everything. I can't even visit him in the hospital unless I get court permission and then the mom makes a big scene in the hospital. I'm trying to stay sober, but I am just holding on by a thread. I gotta get this taken care of so my son's mom and her mom can't continue to use my being on probation against me in court. When I talk about it, I get very emotional, so I don't want to sit in a room with a bunch of strangers and discuss it. But I need to, so thanks for calling me out. And you're right, we all have issues in our lives, and I should be talking about mine."

The group sits quietly for a few moments. Frank acknowledges the intensity of John's challenges. "Man, that hit me like a punch in the gut. I'm glad you shared that with us. You've heard me share about my son and the fact that the stress I experience as a co-parent is my biggest trigger to use, but my stress is nothing compared to what you've got going on. From the people I know who co-parent, it's a tough gig. Hard enough for two different people to agree on what's best for a child, but when there are resentments between the parents, the difficulties multiply. I always say that I have a chance to complete this program unless something happens to James. But you're here, sober. That's incredibly inspiring. All I can do is send good vibes to both of you; anything you need, just ask."

"I'm sorry that I called you out and made you share all of your business," Tom apologizes, "it wasn't my place. I feel like a dick for saying anything."

"I appreciate that," John responds, "but don't feel bad. I was sincere in what I said. I do feel a little relief from sharing it with the group. I have very little opportunity to sneak away from all the problems in my life right now, and hearing that my experience and sobriety can inspire others helps me see outside the present, so thanks, Tom."

Narrative Therapy Externalizing Assignment

Frank begins to share his homework by explaining that it's a Narrative Therapy externalizing assignment. The goal of this assignment is to shift the substance user's perspective from seeing him/herself as the problem to viewing the substance and its use as the problem—a problem separate and apart from the user. To do so, the user chooses an animal/thing to represent the substance and his/her use of it, literally externalizing, or projecting, the experience and effects of the substance use. The assignment poses written questions which the substance user thinks and writes about and then shares his/her answers with the group.

Frank prefaces his homework presentation by acknowledging to the group that he struggled at the beginning of the assignment because he was unsure what, exactly, he was supposed to externalize. Frank explains, "I decided to externalize everything that comes with alcohol. Alcohol itself, the impact it has on me, and drinking as an addiction. Hard not to put them all together, so my externalized animal will mean all these things. I named my alcohol problem 'the chameleon,' because it had a way of hiding itself and its severity from me for many years. Many other people were also unable to see it initially, but even as others' recognition of my drinking increased, I continued to believe it was not the problem. The chameleon would eventually begin to do much more than just allow me to socialize more comfortably. It ultimately camouflaged my intensifying alcoholism and its increasingly deleterious effects on my life, but I was, of course, happily oblivious to its dangers at the time.

I met the chameleon when I was fourteen, but I knew of him earlier as my parents and all their friends also hung out with chameleons, some more than others. I remember the day I met my chameleon with a clarity far beyond my memories of other events in my life during that period—he really helped me unwind and blot out the stress and anger that I had been feeling for years. I can't think of many events in my life afterward in which the chameleon didn't participate. I was unable to see the negative side of the chameleon because everyone else I knew was hanging out with a chameleon too.

I couldn't see that my chameleon allowed me to get into dangerous situations because it would tell me 'it's what everyone does,' and, 'think about how much better you will feel if you just have a drink.' My chameleon had a way of connecting me to people who also had chameleons and I quit hanging out with people who didn't have chameleons similar to mine, some of whom I'd been friends with for years. Despite their long-term importance to me, I chose to disconnect from them. At first the chameleon helped with some of the anger I had, but after a while its presence seemed to add to my anger and I'd find myself doing more dangerous and potentially self-destructive stuff. This became progressively worse as I continued to hang out with it. I began to do things that were inconsistent with my values, but the chameleon helped numb the fear and other inhibitions that I would have experienced without him. When he was gone the next day, I would feel like shit; feelings of shame were part of my life prior to drinking but were taken to new levels by the behaviors and consequences of my time with the chameleon.

I think that deep down I knew that there was something about my relationship with the chameleon that was taking me nowhere, which is one reason I enlisted in the Army at age 17. I thought I'd straighten up with some discipline. And it worked for a while. I did great in basic training. My parents were proud, my brothers and sister were proud, my girlfriend was happy. I didn't bring the chameleon to boot camp and my body and mind responded well.

After boot camp, I was stationed in Germany where it was legal to hang out with your chameleon everywhere at age 18, whereas prior to that its presence and its effects had to be somewhat more concealed. I also had no parental control or familiar people around me. For most of that three-year enlistment I hung out with the chameleon more than I had in the past, as well as with other types of reptiles with which I had previously been unfamiliar. The chameleon would spend my money before I had it, which continued for many years after—and left me with credit issues on top of financial insecurity. The chameleon's impact on money was a significant source of shame for me, and the shame slowly led to depression.

I somehow got an honorable discharge, and the chameleon and I headed back home to Michigan. I moved up to East Lansing, home of Michigan State University, almost immediately, and started another run with the chameleon that was to last for years. The chameleon told me to stay out late and left me to fend for myself in the mornings when I should have been working. This started a years-long streak of losing job after job. The chameleon made sure that it was more important than jobs, relationships, money management, dealing with emotions, family, and soon, my health. At some point in my mid-twenties, I started to hang out with the chameleon to the point of blacking out and I would wake up and realize I'd pissed myself. I think this is the first time I've ever told anyone that. You'd think that this would be an eye-opening experience and help me to see the impact of this relationship, but instead the chameleon helped me cope with the shame of this behavior. The chameleon had this destructive ability to help me avoid or hide what was really going on in my life. This shame and avoidance led to me pissing myself more times than I can guess, in so many places; family and friends' houses, beds with girlfriends, in jails, everywhere. I know it's disgusting because that's exactly how I felt. I tried tricks and things to prevent it, but the chameleon would escort me past those to the point where I had no control over my faculties. I think this was about when people noticed that the chameleon and I shouldn't be invited places, which makes sense in retrospect—I wouldn't have wanted us there either, if it was my house!

"I moved across the country in 2002 with a girlfriend who likely already knew that the chameleon and I were only focused on one another, but the excitement of a move to Portland delayed our breakup. Instead of her leaving me in 2002, it happened a few years later. The breakup was inevitable, because eventually 23-year-olds grow into 27-year-olds who quit falling for bullshit. Which means the chameleon and I would be in the market for a new 23-year-old who hadn't yet seen the impact a chameleon can have on a relationship. At first breakups hurt, but you get to a point where you know it's better for the other person in the long run. When you live with addiction, you learn to manipulate and deceive everyone. Even yourself. The truth is too real and would cause difficult conversations, so the chameleon would help navigate me in directions where I could avoid those discussions.

"Once that long-term relationship was over, I found myself single in a large city with a decent party scene. The chameleon loved this period because he could tell me to go out, and due to my loneliness or inability to be on my own, I needed little convincing. The shame and depression increased, and I would think about leaving the chameleon, but at the most I'd take only mini breaks, and sometimes it was so bad the chameleon would have me convinced the best way out was to try to get hit by a car, so I would actually purposely stumble into traffic. I've literally bounced off several windshields and each time apologized to a terrified driver who thought I was crazy.

"The chameleon would entice me to lock myself in a basement and drink a half gallon of whisky in an effort to end my life, but thankfully I would pass out from the alcohol prior to my doing myself any serious damage. I finally quit listening to the chameleon talk about how depressed we were because I know firsthand what suicide can do to a family. I had a cousin my age who committed suicide when we were seniors in high school. He was the pride and joy of his family and they were crushed; I imagine they still are.

"I hung out at a punk/metal dive bar so often that I ended up getting a job bartending there, which was the chameleon's favorite thing I had ever done. The chameleon was fed every day as though it was at a never-ending buffet, and the scene was filled with people I thought were cool and funny. Being there allowed me to feel better about myself, as many of those cool people had chameleons, too. I was also working at a deli down the street from where I bartended, on the gentrified, hip Alberta Street in Northeast Portland. I would ride my bike up and down that street during the day delivering sandwiches, and one day I went to the bar and was told that one of the owners had nicknamed me Sandwich Frank. My chameleon morphed into that identity and it stuck.

"A few years after forming this new identity, I got a DUI. The same friend who'd nicknamed me Sandwich Frank was trying to call me a cab, but the chameleon was telling me 'it's only a few blocks away' and 'no one tells us what to do.' This was my second DUI but my first in Portland. A week later, the 21-year-old girl I'd been seeing only a few weeks told me she was pregnant. The chameleon was scared; this was a colossal turn of events. But the chameleon continued to direct my brain down the same path of avoidance I'd become accustomed to and I ignored the DUI for at least a year. I also drank all during the pregnancy. I did try to do the right thing after James was born, though. I took care of the DUI by doing a six-month diversion program and got a job at a grocery store deli that was closer to home and had benefits. I worked there full time, so I worked less and less in the bar, until finally I was pouring drinks just one day a week. Then James' mother and I started fighting a lot and the chameleon told me that getting hammered during my bar shift would be a good way to take a break from the stress at home. But obviously that wasn't a good plan, and the bar, my favorite job, eventually fired me. The chameleon was good at showing me how I was the victim in that situation. I drank during every shift I worked, sometimes fought with customers, often failed to perform parts of my job, and frequently forgot to lock the doors when I left. Somehow, however, I believed that it was the bar's owners who were at fault—that it was their lack of compassion that motivated them to fire me. It all seemed very unfair. The chameleon could surely turn a story. A big part of my identity was crushed when I lost that job, as the chameleon and I together had been 'Sandwich Frank.' And even though it clearly wasn't the greatest identity— when I think about it now it's like I was the one getting "sandwiched" into a little sliver of what I could have been doing with my life—it felt as though a part of me died that day. I'd worked there seven years, which was the longest I had ever held a job.

"There was a pervasive unhealthiness to my relationship with my son's mom, so, things at home didn't get any better. The relationship had great moments and I do have some fond memories. We always had lots of love for James. It's challenging, though, to live for someone as you do a child and to simultaneously try to have a healthy relationship with another adult when the chameleon is taking so much of your daily energy. The chameleon gave me permission to totally screw up my life, to prioritize itself over everything else, until my relationship with James' mom was over and my kid, the thing that meant the most to me, was no longer part of my daily life. The chameleon pounced on my depressive state after James' mom and I broke up. One night he nudged me to get out of my house and meet some friends at a bar to watch a slam dunk contest. He murmured the phrase he used to remind me of my own powerlessness: 'It is what it is.' That statement has always had a profound effect on me because it suggests that my circumstances are inalterable and that I have no real agency. My conclusion in the face of these hopelessness-inducing beliefs was that they made me not responsible for trying to change my behavior.

"My attitude might have stayed that way had I not woken up late on the night of the slam dunk festivities in a police station with my third DUI."

The group acknowledges the work that Frank obviously put into his assignment. Caesar shakes his head, remarking, "I've never thought about how I don't remember the period before I first used, but I recall that first day like it was today. I could even tell you what I was wearing. Why is that?"

Primary Counselor explains, "A big part of memory recall is the emotional connection associated with that moment, so if a moment connects to you at a highly emotional place, there's a good chance you'll remember it. But if the intensity of the emotion is too high, as in really traumatic events, sometimes your memory will not let you recall it. In many situations when people use their primary substance for the first time, it relieves pain, or stress, or trauma symptoms and the memory of this incredible freedom from those feelings is stored. And if those painful emotions are triggered again your mind will think 'How do I handle this? Oh I know!' The memory of being on the substance can also be recalled by the opposite feelings—such as the sense of relief or reward you might feel when you get a job or pass a test. So both challenging and joyous emotions can trigger a memory that points you toward using a substance. In some ways, no one has an alcohol or substance issue, they have a memory issue. Anyone else remember how they felt the first time they used?"

A newer peer named Alexis asks, "What's that song that they always play at funerals...ummm, 'Amazing Grace.' You know the lyric that says, 'I once was lost, but now I'm found'? The first time I drank, I felt like I was found." Frank nods in agreement.

8/1/2012
Individual Counseling Session: 60 Minutes

Frank arrives on time for his scheduled appointment. He appears upbeat and excited. Primary Counselor asks, "How have things been since our last session?"

"Things are going well, and I'm glad you asked because I wanted to talk about our last session. I've been thinking a lot about what happened, and I think you did some sort of magic trick and I don't know how you did it."

Primary Counselor responds, chuckling, "I'm intrigued; what is the magic trick you're speaking of?"

"If you remember last time, I was really upset, and I'm sorry if I said something personal or inappropriate—I was just really pissed off and stressed out," Frank begins. "Sometimes we have to wait a few minutes in that waiting room and I swear if I'd had to wait another minute or two, I might have walked out. I was <u>that</u> close, but you were quick and before I could say f-this, I was in your office and I vented."

Primary Counselor nods, reflecting, "You were frustrated. You're allowed to talk about challenging emotions with me."

"Thank you, but I wasn't frustrated when I left," Frank responds. "I walked out of here feeling different, like almost proud. I could see a lot of the positive things that are going on in my life and that it's because I'm sober and working on fixing my life. I couldn't have made such a drastic change in feelings in such a short time by myself—that was the magic—and like most magic, I want to know how you did that."

"It's not enough to have the positive feeling but you also want to know the process of how it happened, is that what you're saying? Because if that's the case, I will tell you the magician's secret, but first you have to tell me why it's so important for you to know."

"I've been thinking about this a lot, and the thought that keeps spiraling in my head is that it has to feel so rewarding to help people become healthier. I don't know, maybe it's something I can do, maybe I could be a counselor," Frank muses, "but I think that would take going to school, which I don't have the time or money to do, and I'm 36."

Primary Counselor interrupts, "Well, what do you think it would feel like if you did the work to be a counselor?"

"I don't even know if I could imagine that feeling," Frank responds, "I've always given up. I think I would be proud, and it would be pretty cool to tell my son that I'm doing something I want to do and for him to see that I'm putting in the hard work required to do it."

"Did you notice the magic trick there?" Primary Counselor inquires.

"No," Frank replies, looking confused.

Primary Counselor explains, "You're having this moment where you're considering making a big change in your life, something that may improve your life and possibly James'. But along with your excitement and enthusiasm, you're experiencing fear about your ability to change. This fear brings self-sabotaging thoughts about the required time and money, and your age; those are the thoughts that keep you stuck, those thoughts are like quicksand. So I quickly changed the subject and asked you to talk about what that change would feel like—to keep you there, in the emotions you experience when you think about the change. Last week you were upset about the challenges of the changes you were making and you were allowing your thoughts to lead you toward quitting, but I didn't let you stay there. I guided you from the negative thoughts about quitting to what changes you've made and the results of those changes. I didn't give you the answers, I simply asked you what changes you've already experienced. You were able to describe many positive examples. Thinking of the improvements you've already seen in your life and this acknowledgement left you feeling different. You know that the good changes are happening. Sometimes, though, fear will try to direct us back to what we're familiar with, even if the familiar makes us unhappy and unhealthy. I didn't tell you that if you worked hard and made this change that you are considering that you would feel proud, you said that because you know that to be true. Imagine your life if you listened to the part of you that knows you can do something rather than the part that tells you that you can't."

"Damn," Frank exclaimed, "that shit is magic, I don't care what you say. That is so cool. Ok, now let me ask you something. You've known me a few months now; do you think I could do this job?"

"Well, you've known me a few months now, so how do you think I would answer that?" counter-questions Primary Counselor with a smile.

Frank chuckles, saying, "You're killing me—how would you answer that? Oh man, I don't know, you don't give answers, you ask questions, so, umm, you'd ask something like, 'Do you think you can do that job or what would you need to do to be able to do that job?' Something like that, right?"

"See there," Primary Counselor reflects, "you're already doing the job!"

Next, Frank brings up the impact on him of John's disclosure around his son's illness and the challenges John has in his relationship with his co-parent, commenting, "That guy's no joke. I mean, I don't know if I could do it. I've got to say that I've been looking at James more and just trying to be grateful. I know some days are tough, but it could be so much worse. He totally makes me want to stay sober. I mean, what am I complaining about? John's story has helped me put what matters back in focus."

Primary Counselor tells Frank his homework for the next two weeks will be to journal about any thoughts he notices that relate to his worry that he's not competent enough to finish a task or reach an objective—the kind of thoughts that keep him from working toward change. He's asked, and agrees, to share his journaling experience in group after it's complete.

8/22/2012
Group Counseling Session: 90 Minutes

Nine members present for group. Frank checks into group by saying that his clean date remains 4/14/12. Frank shares his mood is an eight, stating the reason it's a fairly high number is that "things are going all right, and I got no big concerns." He continues, "I went to a wedding over the weekend; I don't know if I felt an urge to use, but it was uncomfortable. I think I made it worse than it really was. A lot of my friends were there, many of them drinking, but they're people who care about me, and miss me and James. I realized that I have never, as an adult, danced sober, and I was self-conscious about it at the wedding. I told my friend at the wedding that I'd always thought my friends were praising my dancing when they would say 'you should have seen yourself last night!' but in retrospect, it's pretty clear that was absolutely not a compliment!" Frank continues, "I had an out—I'd already told friends that I had to leave the reception at a certain time. So I left early, walked right out and went to a meeting. It worked out fine." He states that his commitment to staying sober is 90%, as he is feeling, "Like I'm in a little bit of a groove." He notes that he has his homework ready to present.

Sharon checks in, reporting that she's feeling, "Frustrated, because my husband—of 26 years—had told me that 'as a gesture of solidarity,' he wouldn't drink while I wasn't drinking. He quit for a while, but then he started to come home a little later than usual, still acting like he isn't drinking, but I could tell the signs that he had been before he even got in the house. I don't understand how people can think that inebriation isn't instantly recognizable, as plain as day. More recently, he's even started drinking in the house, justifying it by saying that it's actually more responsible to drink at home than to drive drunk, as I did. He didn't have to make that remark, that just hurts, and it makes me wonder, 'Where is my credit?' I mean, at least I'm trying to clean up my mess!"

Caesar shares that he, too, immediately notices when people are drinking, and continues, "In retrospect, I wonder a lot what people thought of me when I was drunk and thinking I was so smooth. Since I've gotten sober," he continues ruefully, "I have yet to see a smooth drunk person." To Sharon, he advises, "I would say keep looking out for you and tell people when they hurt you, because you don't have to put up with that. You are being punished by the law, that's not your husband's job."

Sharon responds gratefully, "I know, I know, you're totally right, and thank you."

Journaling Counterproductive Thoughts Assignment

Frank starts his homework presentation to the group by pulling out the journal in which he's recorded thoughts he's noticed during the previous two weeks that keep him stuck by discouraging him from taking the steps necessary to make positive changes in his life. Frank shares that he, "Wrote down a lot of thoughts around smoking. I think a lot about how 'this will be my last one' or 'after this pack I'll quit.' I also justify it with the idea that 'I deserve to smoke as I'm quitting alcohol; I can't stop both at the same time.' I guess these thoughts are winning because I haven't quit and don't see it happening in the near future—ha—that's another one of those thoughts right there.

"I'm also trying to avoid romantic relationships for a while. My goal is to remain single for a year. I've always been a womanizer and I just don't need any distractions right now. Plus, if someone wants to hang out with me with all the baggage I have now, that's a red flag for sure. But I'll have thoughts like, 'Just give her a call,' or 'You should go to such and such store or coffee shop,' when I know it's not about the coffee. I eat at this Thai place by my house and the food's not even that good, but I eat there anyway on Thursdays because the waitress that day is cute. I know schedules and I'm trying not to know schedules. It's not like you can ask someone out when they're working. Not being able to be alone feels like a sickness.

"Other things I tell myself all the time are 'Don't to go to work' or 'Don't go for a run,' but I've been good about not listening to that kind of thought; I'm currently on a last-warning status at work because of spotty attendance, though. All that court stuff and my kid being sick, plus

I missed some days before I stopped drinking because I was hungover. So, I've got to go—work has this policy that if you're late an hour, it's an absence. I take the bus and MAX train from the other side of town. Taking a job that far away sounded like a good idea when I had my moped. I left the house an hour before work the other day and ended up an hour late, and that's an absence. I'm holding myself accountable for it—not blaming it on anyone else—but man, that's a tough one.

"Lately, I've been considering going back to school, but my thinking wavers back and forth between feelings of confidence and excitement and thoughts about how 'I'm too old and missed my chance,' and, 'I'm not smart enough,' plus the reality that I work full time. So that's it today, I have a lot of stuck thoughts around those issues. Some I'm ignoring; others are running the show."

Caesar identifies with Frank's difficulties quitting smoking, "It's so hard; your whole body wants that smoke when you're trying to quit. You tell yourself that you can quit later and convince yourself that it's okay to have that next smoke or pack."

Tom adds, "I get my mind made up on using an addictive substance like cigarettes and I can't even hear any other perspective. My doctor's been saying for ten years now that I need to quit smoking but it doesn't matter because all I hear is, 'Buy a pack.'"

Alexis, who had been unusually quiet since Frank's comments about the waitress, suddenly remarks, "I had a stalker a couple of years ago, from the coffee shop I worked at while I was in college, so that notion of knowing schedules is real—and it's pretty fucking scary."

"I don't think my example is stalking," Frank responds, "we've known each other for a while and we're friends."

"Right, but what about when it's not friendly? If your brain can tell you to keep smoking for ten years when the doctor is telling you to stop, how easy is it for your brain to tell you, 'it's cool, we're friends, she may be into me,' when that's not the case at all? The male brain is scary."

"I'm sorry that offended you," Frank apologizes, "that wasn't my intention, and you're right, I really have never thought of it like that."

Alexis corrects him, "I wasn't offended, just thought this was the place to share it. Most guys don't think of it that way. That's a perk of being a guy."

9/11/2012
Individual Counseling Session: 60 Minutes

Frank arrives on time for his individual session. He shares that his son recently started his second year in a cooperative preschool. Because of the school's inclusive philosophy, all parents have jobs at the school during the year to offset the tuition costs, making it more affordable and allowing parents to participate in the learning environment. He explains that when James' mom moved to the city of Newberg after their relationship ended in January, "I had to do both parents' jobs since she lives an hour away and doesn't drive." Asked how he feels about all of it, Frank answers enthusiastically, "I'm actually excited because the school is great and James loves it. I get to sit in the classroom with all the kids and help, and there's lots of playing on their breaks. It's cool for me to participate in his daily life like that. The other job is to assist in fundraising activities. Last year I killed it in the fundraising department. I planned and coordinated a Heavy Metal concert at the bar I used to work at and the cost of the show plus donations all went to the school. All my friends came out and donated money and we made about $500. I've got some good people on my side; they've always been there for things involving my son. I also arranged a poker game and eighteen people played which brought in another couple hundred dollars. I didn't know I could do that, and it was cool to find skills I didn't know I had, so this year I want to figure out something even bigger. Last year I was making sure I didn't drink the night before I was in the classroom because I didn't want to smell like beer around people's kids—so glad I don't have to worry about that shit any longer. I get to be just a parent among other parents. I haven't had too many relationships with adults that didn't involve drinking, and it's different. I get anxious, I don't know what to do a lot of the time, but when I'm around the kids I don't have to worry about that; I get to be me."

"And you don't get to be you when you're around the parents?" queries Primary Counselor.

"Well, I have this probation going on, so my life outside the school is very different from those of the other parents. They all have careers and cars and they aren't in treatment for alcohol abuse. Even though our kids are in the same class, James is starting behind them in so many ways. I'm glad that he has this school so he can be normal for three days a week and not worry about having separated parents or having to ride the bus so his dad can take a piss test. He gets to practice writing and socialize with friends and play and learn, and he does all of that because I'm taking care of my responsibilities. I could have messed this up, but I haven't. I think all of the parents love the school, but it's especially meaningful to us."

Primary counselor assigns Frank the task of logging his anxiety in social situations for homework.

Specifically, to log his anxious thoughts and note where in his body he feels anxiety. After logging the thought, he is to challenge it by asking himself if he believes the thought is rational or irrational, and why. Part of the assignment is to present it to the group.

9/26/2012
Group Counseling Session: 90 Minutes

Eleven members present for group. Prior to check in, Primary Counselor informs group members that Tom will no longer be in group and offers members time to process the news if they feel the need for it.

Sharon is the first to respond, "I don't know if you all realized this, but Tom and I were the two oldest members of this group. We also rode the bus together and he became a friend. He's actually a pretty funny guy. He just wasn't ready to give this a chance, which is why he's back in jail."

Primary Counselor interrupts Sharon to remind the group, "This is a time to process our own feelings and thoughts, rather than to talk about what may or may not have happened to Tom."

"I get what you're saying," Randy interjects, "but it's hard not to connect the two. We all know what happened so we might as well talk about it in the group rather than gossiping outside the group. I don't know about anyone else, but Tom's mistakes are a good example to me that this is real and there are consequences if we don't figure it out."

"I talked to him and he told me to tell people here what he did, so they don't screw this up," Sharon agrees, "So, is it okay to tell the group?"

"Okay, go ahead," assents Primary Counselor.

Sharon explains that Tom crashed his car on the previous Thursday while intoxicated. He was not supposed to be driving, didn't have a license, and his car was not insured. Tom has now been released and is awaiting a trial but is in serious legal trouble and more than likely will be going to prison. He told me that he wishes he'd taken this opportunity we've all been given and said it's clear to him in hindsight how smart we all are for taking this seriously." The group mood becomes somber, with many members acknowledging that it could easily have been one of them in that situation.

Frank checks into group, saying his clean date remains 4/14/2012. He shares his mood is a six, explaining that he's starting to feel better after having the flu but had to miss a day of work. "I haven't gotten to run in a week, plus being sick, I can tell I'm off—just not feeling myself. And I've been irritated." Frank states that his commitment to staying sober is 80 percent. "Already don't feel good so no need to feel any worse, and now hearing that about Tom… I can't imagine what he's going through." Frank reports that he has homework ready to present.

Caesar checks in, revealing that this is his last group. Group members congratulate him and several give feedback around his steadying force in the group and the fact that he's made the whole experience more bearable. "I'm relieved that I was able to make it through the treatment part of the program and now have more time to be at home with my family," Caesar responds. He also affirms that "This group has been helpful; I've learned a lot from all the people before and after me." And finally, "If you see me out there, don't walk by me like you don't know me, cuz I'm gonna grab you all and give you a hug and find out what's up with ya'll."

Journaling Social Anxiety Thoughts Assignment

Frank is asked to present his homework. He prefaces his presentation with a description of the assignment. "I was asked to record in my journal instances when I experienced social anxiety, where I felt that anxiety in my body, and whether my thoughts around the given situation were rational or irrational." Frank explains that he's had only a few situations in the previous two weeks during which "I was around people with whom I'm relatively unfamiliar and not very comfortable. That's when I get the most anxiety; when I'm around a group of people and I don't know what to do, or I feel that I must go and talk to people I don't know. If I know you, I have no issues. Like, right now, I'm cool, but I just get awkward in some social situations. I had this meeting with some of the parents at the preschool a few weeks ago; some of them I know but a bunch I don't. There were a few different small break times when everyone was chatting with everyone else and I'm sitting there looking like an asshole. I feel like a kid who's around adults, like I don't know what I'm doing. I felt nervous and had butterflies in my stomach, so I tried to find a way out. I went to the bathroom; then I thought about faking a phone call. I have thoughts like 'they know I don't know how to do this adult stuff,' which make me more nervous. The worst is when you've got a person you feel comfortable with, but they know other people there, so the person drifts off to socialize and they leave you alone, and it feels like you're on a stage. Or at least that's how I feel. I think that the other parents are looking down at me or somehow know that I split from my son's mom and are judging me. I think that most of these thoughts are irrational because nobody has treated me badly or weirdly, and most people actually seem to enjoy talking to me. I think I just get anxious and make things up." Frank continues, "I get the same way at AA meetings. I know that the whole recovery thing is to build a new social circle and be friends with all these people. But all of them are already best friends who have coffee, have dinner, talk about their parties for so and so and all this shit. I can't even have a five-minute conversation with people after a meeting because I don't know what to say. I just have this imposter thing. I feel like I'm not like the other parents; I go to AA but I don't feel like I fit in there either; my anxiety is about being revealed as a fraud. I'm waiting for everyone to turn and look and say, 'you're a drunk-driving, deadbeat, alcoholic dad and you should get the hell out of here!' I leave 12-Step meetings as soon they're over because I feel all tense. When I know people, I'm outgoing, and I think of myself as someone who connects with other people pretty deeply, but it takes the right environment to create that. Even though I understand intellectually that all this is irrational, it still feels real. I know that most those folks in AA are just like me, and none of us are pieces of shit, but it's part of what we tell ourselves."

Alexis interjects that she's always had anxiety, "I used to get panic attacks when I felt like I couldn't control a situation. Coming to this group the first time freaked me out, and it still does to some extent, which is why I always sit next to the door. I've been meditating this last year and I find it helps; I haven't had a panic attack in over a year. I also drank a lot but haven't in the last three months. I danced ballet for years as a child but eventually quit because I would tell myself that all the other girls were better and prettier to the point of panic almost every day. I miss it—the dancing—not the freaking out part, so I get the imposter thing you're talking about."

John shares that his anxiety is "off the charts, worrying about my son and not being able to see him," and reveals, "I'm lucky if I get four hours of sleep a night. I've tried supplements, but they haven't helped. The only thing that has ever helped was drinking, because the alcohol would numb my feelings so that I could pass out. I just try to remain positive and think positive thoughts. If I notice negative thoughts, I have to start telling myself positive thoughts about my son's future—'he is going to have a normal life, he is going to have fun with other kids,'—things like that; if I didn't, the stress would be too much."

10/17/2012
Group Counseling Session: 90 minutes

Eleven members present for group. Frank checks into group, stating his clean date remains 4/14/2012. He shares his mood as a nine, explaining, "I got my six-month chip on Sunday." He passes his chip around the group and the members give him a round of applause. Frank states that his commitment to staying sober is 90 percent. "After I got my chip on Sunday, I went out and ran nine miles, which was my longest run yet. I'm happy with where I am right now." Frank finishes his share by saying that he doesn't have homework to present.

"What's the biggest surprise to come from these last six months?" Randy asks him.

Frank laughs a little, "Well, the running is crazy. I didn't see that coming at all, so I'm excited to have found this outlet. But the thing people don't ever talk about, probably because it's gross, is the pooping." The group starts to laugh. "Seriously, my poop process was disgusting before I got sober. It was like a witch's cauldron down there. But now I have regular looking poop; it's a perk. More people would seriously consider quitting if they knew how much better that part of their lives would be!"

11/6/2012
Individual Session: 60 Minutes

Frank shows up for his appointment on time. Asked if he
wants to talk about losing his job (in a previous group,
he'd shared that he'd recently been fired and was upset
and stressed out by it), Frank responds, "Well, it sucks.
I was doing some of the best work there that I'd done at
any job. My coworkers and bosses were bummed and
reached out, but my bosses' hands were tied. I was on
a contract that didn't allow another absence, and the
previous Monday, I had woken up an hour late and knew
I wasn't going to be in before my first hour was over,
which as you know counts as an absence. My kid also
wasn't feeling well so I stayed home, knowing they were
going to fire me. The funny thing is the Detroit Tigers,
my favorite sports team, got swept in the World Series
on Sunday. That night I ate a good dinner and went to
bed early, ready to get that behind me. I think I screwed
up the AM/PM on my alarm because it never went off.
When the store manager and I talked about the decision,
I told him not to worry, this wasn't even the worst thing
that happened to me this week; the Tigers losing hurt
much more than this."

"You seem to be taking this in stride," Primary
Counselor observes. "How are you coping with it?"

"That's kind of the crazy thing. I was immediately
stressed out, but I will more than likely get

unemployment, which will help. I know I've got to look around for something else. So, I went to this Veteran's Job Fair this past weekend to see about finding something, and it sucked. It was completely humbling. I mean, I've got no skills and these jobs are all for skilled employees. This guy asked me how I'd like to be an engineer. I said I'd love to, but the problem is that I'm not one. I told him if any of those engineers needed sandwiches, though, then I could help out! So, I'm feeling bummed and I'm walking out of the place like Charlie Brown, head down, kinda dragging my feet, when this woman hands me a piece of paper. I start reading it and it's information about this government program called VRAP, the Veteran's Retraining Assistance Program. It says if you meet the criteria, you could be awarded some educational benefits to go back to school for a year. I'm reading the criteria: 35 and over—check; unemployed—oh shit—two for two; got an honorable discharge, boom, not getting other military compensation, and not enrolled in state or federal training. I ain't enrolled in shit! I was on the bus kind of freaking out. I qualify for this program, and for the last few months I've been thinking about going back to school for counseling, but I couldn't get past how I would ever be able to simultaneously work and go to school. If I get this, it'll supplement our living expenses enough to allow me to focus on school—to learn to be a student—to give this a real shot and not something I fuck up or quit. I'm pretty stoked, and I've already submitted the application so now I'm just waiting."

Primary Counselor responds, "I can feel your excitement. Can I ask how you would have handled this if you had still been drinking?"

"I would have been pissed about losing my job. I would have blamed my employer, then I would have gotten wasted," relates Frank with certainty, "I would have gotten another job I didn't like doing, and I would have repeated the process. I might still have gone to this job fair, but I would not have been considering school, so I would've just read the first sentence of that paper and trashed it. I've got this spiritual feeling about this, and I don't get many of those. At least I don't notice many of those, but this is just too obvious. This could be a chance to have a career—a job I can be proud of and my son can be proud of. I'm getting healthier, I've lost a bunch of weight, I'm running a lot, and I'm not as angry. But this is part of it; if I must give up drinking because I suck at it, then I may as well try to help others who suck at it. I know, pretty profound," Frank observes self-deprecatingly, and then apologizes for his observation, "sorry, but you know what I'm saying."

"I do know what you're saying, and many people who begin a life of recovery find many things in their lives that allow them to feel happy, proud, empowered and effective," Primary Counselor replies, "A recovery lifestyle promotes self-efficacy.

"What is that, self-efficacy?" asks Frank.

"Self-efficacy is the belief in yourself that you can make the changes that will improve your life. For example, many people understand they need to stop drinking, but when you start to believe that you can consistently take the daily actions needed to maintain a non-drinking lifestyle, your confidence in your abilities and your determination to overcome obstacles increases. Are you starting to believe that you have the ability to meet your goals?"

"I don't know if I would go that far. I mean, if I go back to school I would have to learn to type; I type like that bobbing chicken thing, one finger at a time," Frank starts to respond before being cut off by Primary Counselor.

"I would like you to answer the question without the negative self-talk or self-deprecating humor. Do you believe in yourself? Do you believe you can meet the goals that you're giving yourself?"

Frank thinks about it momentarily, "I have some friends who had this saying when we were in our early 20's, 'expect the worst and then you won't be disappointed.' It was one of those things that you make jokes about when things go wrong, but that way of thinking became almost like a religion for me and I've been telling myself that for almost 15 years. And you know what's happened—a lot of the worst! I've now got this brief period where things have been going all right; even losing a job has the benefit of qualifying me for student aid, even the DUI that necessitated my participation in this program has brought benefits. Maybe there have always been benefits to all the hardships I experienced that I couldn't see. I must be told not to answer questions without talking shit about myself because I do it so much, and I don't want to do that any longer. I don't know if my shifting beliefs reflect a mental change or just having a brain and body that are functioning better, but instead of telling myself I can't do something, I'm at a place where I'm thinking, 'why the fuck can't I?' which is a pretty fun perspective on life."

Frank is asked to complete an assignment around shame. It consists of reading *The Gifts of Imperfection* by Brené Brown and thinking about the specific shame beliefs that he repeats to himself most often. The assignment includes noting how he feels when he has those common thoughts, and what behaviors they lead to. Frank is also told to hypothesize where his shame thoughts might have originated. Finally, the project includes writing some counter-statements that can replace his shame thoughts, and imagining what potential behaviors they could lead to.

11/21/2012
Group Counseling Session: 90 minutes

Ten members present for group. Frank checks into group saying his clean date remains 4/14/12. He shares his mood is an "eight," reporting happily, "I found out that I meet the criteria for the veterans' assistance educational benefits, so I'm registering for classes and will start in January!" Frank states that his commitment to staying sober is 95 percent. "I'm so excited for this chance. I also know that my decision to discontinue school in the first place is one I made while drinking, so if I were to start using again, I would be starting another cycle of being excited for an opportunity and then drinking it away." Frank indicates that he's ready to present his homework.

A new peer, Kenny, shares that he's been sober for six months and has been going to school off and on for almost two years, stating "So many things are easier when you're sober. You have a lot more energy, for one thing, which is good, because even though sobriety is way less complicated than the alternative, fulfilling my responsibilities as a sober person requires some serious effort. When I'm drinking, I can find any reason to put off homework—and then there I am, sitting in a class, confused by the lesson—just throwing lots of tuition money away."

Sharon reports that she recently changed jobs. "A friend I met through AA told me about a job opening in her company and introduced me to the hiring coordinator. I had been at the company I just left for ten years but was feeling burned out for the last few. I was nervous about starting a new job after doing my old one for so long, but this new opportunity is allowing me to be creative and I feel excited at work again."

John checks in, saying, "I got my 90-day coin and can't believe how difficult staying sober has been with everything I've had going on. The worst part is that my son's mom and her mom are the ones making it so difficult for me to spend time with my son. This while they're both using—they drink, they smoke—but somehow, I'm the one who needs to be monitored. They want me to fail; I'm the father of their son/grandson and they want me to fail so they can win, whatever that means to them. I cannot understand that, but I got 90 days without using anything, and it's documented."

Journaling Shame Thoughts Assignment

Frank, asked to share his homework, responds "I haven't started the book I'm supposed to read because there's a long hold on it at the library, but I'm on the list for it. I did the assignment anyway and will read the book when I can get it. I was supposed to write the most common shame thoughts I have. The things I tell myself the most are 'You're a piece of shit,' 'It is what it is,' 'You can't do this/that,' and simply, 'Fuck it.' I've been telling myself these things for as long as I can remember. Each has a specific meaning about who I am, how things can't be changed, that I'm powerless to improve my life, and that I should, therefore, quit trying. Usually when I'm having these thoughts I feel worthless, depressed, defeated, and angry. These thoughts and feelings paralyze me. I don't start things or I quit working on things I've started—I talk myself out of trying. I drink, I isolate, I accept a life that I'm unhappy with. I was asked to come up with some counter-statements to use when I notice myself having these thoughts. I told Primary Counselor the other day that instead of talking myself out of taking action, I've been repeating this new, hopeful question to myself. It's 'Why can't I do this?'" Frank pauses for a moment before correcting himself humorously, "My actual phrasing is, 'Why the fuck can't I?' but since I'm going back to school I have to quit cussing every time I speak.

"I think learning about addiction has helped me understand that a lot of my issues have little to do with whether I'm a piece of shit or not. I clearly have this disease, so I'm accepting of that and not beating myself up over it. Having this acceptance, I can say to myself, 'You do have a brain disease.' I also can ask myself, regarding whatever hurdle I'm facing, 'What's the first thing I need to do to surmount it?' This helps me be solution-focused, something that's already made me feel more powerful and competent. Another part of the assignment requires explaining how these new thoughts foster different behaviors. I think they give me confidence and hope and inspire me to try my best to move toward my objectives, something that leads me to accomplish many more of my goals. I really can't wait to start accomplishing things: this treatment, this program, school, whatever comes next; they will all bring obstacles I need to overcome. In the past, I wouldn't take care of issues, and those unresolved issues fueled my drinking.

"Lastly, I was supposed to try to figure out where this shame-based thinking comes from. I think that my dad leaving when I was five had an impact. I was the oldest of three kids, and I think I believed that his actions resulted from something that I had done or just who I was. He didn't call or write and I only saw him a few times in the next thirty years. My mom and stepdad, who were there paying the bills and taking care of the adult stuff, also drank a lot and many times would leave work and go straight to the bar for hours, often retuning after we were already asleep. I regularly wondered what was so wrong with us that they wouldn't want to come home to see us. But we never got to talk about those things as a family.

I also had this horrible experience in fourth grade. I lived in a poorer part of our school district near an area we called 'the projects.' In fourth grade there were two classrooms that were divided; one had all the kids from the projects and the other all the other kids from the other streets. Our classroom had the kids who got in trouble, who were poorer, whose parents were less inclined to give a shit. And did they give this bunch of kids who needed the most attention a *Stand and Deliver* teacher who cared? Nope, that's for the movies. No, we got a teacher who was an alcoholic. And how do a bunch of fourth graders know this information about their teacher? Because some of us learned what it looked like at home. We were also aware of it just because it was common knowledge. This teacher would be passed out in her car before class. We would knock on the car window to rouse her to come to class. Her car, which was a brown Smokey and the Bandit Pontiac Trans-Am, had dozens of empty bottles on the floor of the back seat. Once inside, she would make the entire class face the front of the classroom and she would sit in the back with her head down on the desk. If any student looked backwards, the student sitting in the seat directly behind that student was supposed to do this swirling finger gesture that meant turn around—we actually practiced this shit. She had this huge Macy's-like shopping bag next to her desk almost every day that had money in it; change—ones, and fives. We would all steal it and she never said a word about it. None of the students ever told anyone about her drunkenness because we didn't want to lose the money. Some of us would sneak out of class and go outside for hours and then just walk back into class like nothing happened. I couldn't make this shit up if I tried. We had this assignment where we had to learn a multiplication problem and show the class; the only damn thing I learned that year was eight times eight = 64! I moved the next year to a new school, not due to this, but because my stepdad built a house on some land he owned in another district. As soon as school started, I could tell I was behind all the other students. I think this is when I started to make jokes and be funny—as a way to hide the fact that I was dumb. I had already developed this shame from my dad leaving and my parents' drinking, so this only made it worse. I mean, the school put all of us in that class knowing she was drunk, and they put us in there because we didn't matter. How're you going to feel like you are something if all these areas of your life tell you that you're not? I think all these things helped me create this story about myself that I was not worth their love or time. Throw in my addiction and the consequences of how I lived, and you have a person who has not been a big fan of himself for decades. And the reality is that when you're looking, you can always find reasons to hate yourself."

John shares that he identifies with the story, "I've been personalizing so much about my past and how it's affected my life and I'm not allowing for much grace or forgiveness. I need to do that; maybe I can create replacement thoughts to help me through this."

"I grew up with a mom who constantly criticized me," Sharon relates, "my weight, my looks, my parenting. She did it up to the time she passed away. It was painful to wonder if she even loved me. I think it's normal for children to believe what their parents say, which is why with my kids I try to praise the effort they put into the things they care about. I try to stay away from appearance stuff, but effort and creativity are two things I praise my children for often."

12/18/2012
Individual Counseling Session: 60 Minutes

Frank arrives on time for his appointment. He'd been late for that week's group session which had resulted in a probation violation. Primary Counselor asks him to share what happened and the consequences of it.

"I just got in some trouble when the MAX train was delayed. From what I've been told, there were three of us who all missed group because of that. I've learned to leave early; I always catch the bus and MAX prior to the one that gets me here in time. I'd rather be 25 minutes early, smoking in front of the building, than trying to open the locked door five minutes after the session starts. Being late is a terrible feeling and triggers my anger and I want to start yelling about fairness, and I always think I have a good argument. So I get on the MAX to head home and during the ride I calm down some and decide I'm going to call my case manager and leave a message so she hears about my absence from me first. I tell her that I was on the MAX, it had issues and I was five minutes late. She called me the next day and told me she appreciated my taking responsibility for what happened; she also said that the two other guys who also missed group failed to do so. She told me I'd have a court date this morning, which I went to before I came here. I've been there before; got a night in jail the last time I thought I was right and expressed I felt life wasn't fair. I know sometimes they let you do community service to make it right, so this weekend I went and did eight hours at Meals on Wheels. I was sitting in court today and listened to ten people go before me, most trying to be slick and playing the victim, not recognizing that this judge has seen all this before. You can't fool the judges, and even if you do, you'll end up in front of them again because you get cocky. I stood up and said I had been five minutes late for group, but I was supposed to be there 15 minutes early, so I was technically 20 minutes late. I explained that I had tried to be proactive and hold myself accountable and went to Meals on Wheels and volunteered for eight hours and got the volunteer sheet signed. The Judge thanked me and said I was 'a breath of fresh air,' and told me that she remembered me from the last time I was in court. She said I was obviously learning to take responsibility for my actions in the program and I should keep it up. Then she excused me, and I walked out of there with a little swagger."

"What lessons have you learned from this that you can transfer to your recovery?" asks Primary Counselor.

"I have to hold myself accountable for my mistakes and own my behavior. Life's not fair sometimes, and I got too much going on right now to be wasting time worrying about the fairness of life. This major crisis, which is how it first appeared, was solved in less than a week and with minimal effort. I like going to Meals on Wheels. I get to do it to help pay off some of my court fines, and the older folks are funny. I grew up around an American Legion so I get them, and I can make them laugh. Plus, they're grateful I'm there, which makes me feel good."

"When you saw the others in the court room engaging in thinking errors like Minimization, Victim Stance, and Justification, could you see your own progress?"

"I thought for a few minutes about how long I had sounded just like that, and how that was exactly the way I used to think. I went to jail for a night a few months ago because of the injustices I saw against me. Blaming others is really a way to avoid looking at my part in situations. I'd rather be aware of my warped thinking any day than be oblivious to it. Most of the other people in court had friends or family with them, supporting their false narratives. We can always find someone who will support our madness. It would've been great if one of those supporters had gotten up and said, 'Oh hell no, you ain't going to be up here acting like an ass in front of this judge,' but nope, the enablers sit in the courtroom, rubbing the backs of their companions— the defendants—and confirming their victimhood in the face of an unjust court system, sympathetically repeating phrases like, 'You never had a chance.'"

Primary Counselor asks Frank about his safety plan for the holidays.

"I'm mostly going to chill. My friends invited James and me over for dinner and they're going to keep it alcohol free, which is really cool because we drank all the time together and I've noticed that a lot of people I drank with don't really talk to me now. I get it; you don't drink to be uncomfortable and hanging out with me can be uncomfortable, for both of us. But these friends mean a lot to me, so the gesture shows some solid support and brings some normalcy to my son, as we've often spent holidays with them. When James isn't with me, I plan to hit up meetings and go for runs. It kind of gets lonely this time of year and that makes me think about how nice it would be to hang out with a woman, but that's not something I need to be doing, and the places I would go to look for one would probably be risky. I got a 24-hour gym membership so I can go hang out on a treadmill and get away from any risky thoughts or feelings. I told a lot of family members I'm sorry for the way I've been over the years. I don't know if they buy this yet because they haven't seen my new behavior in action, but I'm grateful that they listened."

Primary Counselor asks Frank to create a goals list for the upcoming year. To create "SMART" Goals, each goal must fit distinct criteria; it must be: specific, measurable, achievable, relevant, and time bound. To arrive at optimal goals, you must determine why each is important to your recovery. Then you create a poster-board showing your goals and present it to the group. Lastly, you hang that poster-board in a visible area of your home for that year.

1/9/2013
Group Counseling Session: 90 minutes

Ten members present for group. Frank checks into group, confirms his clean date remains 4/14/2012. He shares his mood is an eight, and expands on his positive feelings, "I started school yesterday. It was cool. Community college is all right and there are lots of people my age." Frank states that his commitment to staying sober is "90 percent; I don't intend to screw this up." He notes that he has his homework ready to present.

Randy shares that the current group will be his last as he is graduating from treatment. "I'm ready to put all these skills and knowledge to work. I think I can apply for a hardship license so I can drive to work, must get a blow-and-go but it'll be worth it not to have my wife drive me around any longer. She deserves a break, for more reasons than just acting as my chauffeur; for all the stuff before that. Just want to say to (Primary Counselor) how much I appreciate you not judging me. I told you some things I've not told anyone else and you never made me feel bad about it, you made it easy to share some hard stuff. And all of you who make up Wednesday nights, I never wanted to come, but I was always glad I did. I've been called out in this group and called other people out, but from a place of caring and from personal experience with substance-related obstacles. I won't forget this."

"I've always felt like you were a son," Sharon responds, "sometimes I wanted to hug you and sometimes I wanted to kick you in the butt. You said in group once 'what if all that stuff I thought I was right about, I was wrong?' I'm a lot older than you, I have a lot more things that I have thought I was right about. That statement makes me think every single day. You probably didn't know that it had such a strong effect on me. When you share what you're thinking, Randy, you can really influence others to grow; don't stop doing that just because you don't have Wednesdays any longer."

SMART Goals for Upcoming Year Outline Assignment

Frank is asked to present his homework. He describes the assignment, which is to outline his SMART Goals for the upcoming year. He pulls out a poster-board with four even sections drawn on it. "I think my year's priorities fall into these four categories: my son, running, school, and family. The first goal is to have James finish his last year of preschool and transition into his first year of kindergarten. I have jobs at his preschool that I need to be on top of. One of them is finishing the substantial amount of work required to get us ready for our big February fundraising auction. My fundraising team built three wooden playhouses; they are so sick! One of them is in my backyard and needs to be painted and finished. It's been a lot of me sitting in the backyard smoking and painting with a friend of mine who's not part of the school. I need to finish it by February 12th, which means I need to spend at least two hours per week on it until it's done. I've already arranged transportation of the playhouse to the auction. I'm also helping prepare the food that will be served at it. My friend is creating the menu and we'll prepare the food the day of the auction. This will complete my responsibilities, with the exception of helping in the classroom twice a month. I need to complete the application for my son to attend a Japanese Immersion school close to my house. It's due on February 27th. I've begun filling it out and have a finish date of January 31st. I will then have to prepare for kindergarten in the fall. I plan to ask family members beforehand for gift cards to stores to help with school supplies. I'm also signing up to be a t-ball coach this spring, which means I need to buy a bike and a tag-along to get us to practice and back quicker than the bus. I'll use my income tax refund to buy them before the start of the season.

Next, my schooling. I will complete at least 46 credits this year, broken down into four quarters so I'm taking twelve credits each term, except for summer when I'll take ten. I'll do all my homework and all my reading. I will attend all classes unless there is no way possible. I'll be prepared for class before I start. I will reach out to other students to form study groups. I'll use math labs as much as necessary. I will get no less than a 3.75 GPA this year. I'll also work with an academic advisor to make sure I meet the requirements to get into the alcohol and drug counselor program.

I will run at least twenty miles per week. I'll run the 15K Shamrock Run in March and train for my first marathon in October. I will ride the bike to class as much as possible. I'll continue to use the gym. I will try to eat less sugar. I've signed up for the online support through 1-800-Quit-Now to prepare to quit smoking and I will start using the patch. I will drink five cups of water per day.

I will purchase tickets for James and me to visit my family in Michigan in June when both of our school terms are done. I've told all family members and none of them will plan other trips at that time. My parents have agreed to drive from the U.P. downstate to Battle Creek, Michigan. I will focus that time on James getting to play with his cousins.

I will also complete treatment and continue recovery work, but I didn't put that here because I think this covers the main points of what will support my recovery. If this year goes as planned, it will be the best year of my life."

After Frank finishes the presentation, group members offer feedback. "What triggers do you need to plan for when you go to Michigan?" Sharon asks.

"I anticipate awkwardness around my parents' drinking. My brothers and their families are fine; they drink but going without it for a few days is fine with them, they're normies. I have some friends I'm going to see but I'll see them all in one shot, at a pool party with kids. I should be okay; I know where meetings are but I feel my brother's house will be safe."

"How long is a marathon?" Kenny queries. Learning from Frank that it's 26.2 miles, Kenny barks, "That's crazy man! You smoke, how the hell you going to do that? Why the hell *would* you do that?"

"I don't know man," Frank laughs, "all those years of drinking, I got used to torturing my body, kind of want to keep doing it, just in a healthy way. I actually thought it would be funny to have a race for runners who still smoke, to see who the fastest smoking runner is!"

"There's a word for someone who wants to be tortured," comments Sharon, "masochist."

"I can't believe how much you can pack into a year when you're not drinking," Alexis remarks, continuing, "I don't have kids and I'm glad I don't; that's a lot of responsibility I'm grateful not to have yet. I would be parenting on my own right now because I'm attracted to guys who have little ambition and are not responsible. Doing that whole assignment was like birth-control for me."

2/5/2013
Individual Session: 60 Minutes

Frank arrives on time for his scheduled appointment. When asked by Primary Counselor how he's doing and if he's making progress on his SMART Goals, Frank replies enthusiastically, "Well, the auction is in two weeks and I'm already almost done building and painting the playhouses. I'm going to buy one at the auction for my son; I painted it the same colors as his room—Detroit Tiger blue and orange. It will be such a relief when I'm done. Besides that, school is going great. I'm loving having homework and things to keep me busy. I'm taking a keyboarding class—it's so challenging because of my lack of typing experience. Thought the first term was a smart time to take it. Taking math—I learned that you've really got a way to go when your math class is just called 'math,' instead of trigonometry or calculus whatever. I have a sociology class that's so cool; I really like seeing the bigger picture of how elements of society influence one another—how one little piece can have a ripple effect that is felt by the whole."

"Where have you seen smaller things fit into a larger whole in your recovery?" Primary Counselor queries.

"I got 90 days sober a few weeks ago, and last year around this time I was looking up lawyers who would help me fight my DUI. A friend recommended this lawyer; I went to see him and we had a long talk—

about more than legal issues—about life and family. I went back and was going to write him a check for the initial amount, but it was like 3,000 dollars that I couldn't afford, and then he told me, "Frank, I'm okay taking your check and representing you and trying to make this as legally painless as possible. However, from our talk, you seem to care about your son a lot. You also seem to know you have some issues with alcohol. Just know if you go this route and don't address the alcohol, the next time you drink and drive you could kill yourself or someone else, and your son will be forced to live with that. Why don't you take the next couple days to think about it? If you decide to hire me and fight this case, we'll move forward. But if what you want is to get better. . ." Frank pauses, and then continues, "I was kind of floored by this. I thought about it and called the District Attorney's office the next day and asked about other options—those that involve treatment. A few weeks ago, I had to go downtown to see my case manager, so I went to an AA meeting at a place I hadn't been to before. And I saw that lawyer there! His recovery allowed him to see my issue and instead of taking my money, he helped me choose a different kind of option. That is some solid integrity. I'm now nine months sober and my child's life is better, and my kid's friends can come over and it's a healthy environment. I go to his preschool and hang out with other families and I'm a positive factor in their lives. Plus, I'm starting school to learn how to help people with their addictions as a counselor. None of it would have happened if I hadn't gotten the DUI and then ended up talking to a lawyer who, unbeknownst to me, had both integrity and an understanding of alcohol abuse. That small conversation started some amazingly positive momentum in my life and the lives of those connected to me."

Asked by Primary Counselor what his principal motivation for going to see the lawyer was, Frank replies immediately, "That's easy—to get my ass out of trouble."

"Would it have worked?"

"Maybe," replies Frank thoughtfully, "but getting out of trouble doesn't keep you out of trouble."

"What about now? What do you think is your primary motivation?"

After considering for a few moments, Frank answers, "Just to make progress today. I have to trust that this will give my son and me a chance for a different life. I want my son to see that life offers him choices and he doesn't have to follow the cycle of addiction. I want him to believe that he's capable of making a good life for himself."

Primary Counselor finishes the line of questioning by asking, "Is your current plan aligned with your primary motivation?"

"Yes, because my plan is preparing for the long-term by focusing on what can be done today," is Frank's confident reply.

Frank is asked to think about what potential setbacks, in the forms of challenging emotions and risky thoughts, he might encounter in recovery; to write them down and then come up with plans to remain safe and sober in these circumstances. He'll be asked to present the results to group three weeks later. Frank acknowledges that he understands the assignment.

2/27/2013
Group Counseling Session: 90 minutes

Eleven members present for group. Frank checks into group, saying his clean date remains 4/14/2012. He shares his mood as a "seven," explaining, "I'm a little tired from school, but still doing ok. I've finished everything involved with the preschool auction and the playhouses were a big hit. I bought the playhouse I had been painting for three hundred and twenty bucks and it's in my front yard. We catered the entire menu all day Saturday, and it was crazy how much food we made. I'm glad that's over and done." Frank states that his commitment to staying sober is "95 percent, I'm rolling right now." He states that he has his homework ready to present.

The newest peer, Sam, checks in, saying he's "Upset about all this—I don't miss work, been with the same person for eight years, own a home, had the same job for ten years. I got two DUIs in eight years, one I blew a .08, the other one I was sleeping in my car. I was drunk, but that's why I was sleeping and not driving. I shouldn't have to do all this; I don't have any problem with alcohol."

Sharon responds, "I think we all understand the frustration you're going through—many of us have had similar thoughts. And you may not have any problem with alcohol. We don't know you, we aren't judges. The reality of your situation is that you're here, same as us, having to do the same things we are; the more accepting of this you are, the easier it will be and the more you can get from it. I've learned a whole lot from this group and much of it has little to do with alcohol. I'm at least twenty years older than everyone else here and one of only two women, and I can connect to the people who come into this room. John over there has a son who's sick, like sick-sick, and he shows up each week, participates as he can, and laughs a few times every group. Whenever I start thinking about the unfairness of it all, I think about that."

Plan for Potential Recovery Setbacks Assignment

When asked to present his homework, Frank explains its purpose as constructing a plan for how to deal with potential setbacks in his recovery. "Well, this kind of goes along with what Sharon was saying regarding John. I think the scariest thing for me would be if something were to happen to my son. Whether a health issue or something custody related, I would probably suddenly have to deal with all kinds of really difficult emotions. I'm sure I would feel sad, powerless, ashamed, and scared. Worry thoughts would negatively affect my sleep. I think some reactions I could have that could threaten my sobriety might be thinking, 'Fuck it! I deserve a drink!' 'This isn't fair,' or 'This is my fault.' I think when I start blaming myself, I'm in trouble. I would have to consciously remember to ask or tell myself very different things, like, 'This is fixable,' 'What do I need to do to accept this?' or, 'What can I do now?' I could go for a run when I'm stressed. I could talk to someone. I don't currently have a sponsor or too many people in recovery to reach out to, although I'm hoping to change that. Luckily, I have lots of close, supportive friends I can talk to.

"I think another area that carries the potential for problems is my dependence on running to reduce my stress, balance myself emotionally, and think things through. It's my space to work on myself and whatever my concerns are at any given time. If I were to get hurt, that might create a challenge. I would probably be left feeling anxious, stressed and worried. Depending on how I got hurt, I might also feel ashamed. This would almost certainly lead to a self-destructive narrative made up of thoughts like, 'You're a failure,' 'You'll never get back to where you were,' or, 'You can't handle this.' These kinds of thoughts would put me at a higher risk of relapse. A contrasting narrative I could use to replace the above negative self-talk with more solution-focused beliefs might include phrases/questions like 'You've dealt with harder things,' 'What do you enjoy doing besides running?' or 'You can do rehab; this injury isn't the end of the world.' I do know I need to develop options in addition to running that help me relieve stress and sharpen my focus. I've never done meditation, but from what I've read, that could be something that helps reduce stress and anxiety.

"Really, the only other thing I can think of as a potential setback would be if I were to fail in school.

I've burned out on a lot of things in the past, so I know I must continue to act with conscious discipline. I could get stressed, insecure, exhausted, burned out. I could have quitting thoughts like, 'This is too hard,' 'Maybe I'm not smart enough to do this,' or 'I should take a term off.' I need to counter those fears with, 'It should be hard,' 'It's not about being smart, it's about whether you do the work,' 'I've taken enough time off,' or, 'James is watching me.' I can't think about the whole process at once, just take care of the upcoming week, find time to get everything done. I've been going to math labs for extra help, which allows me to really master the concepts we're studying. This, in turn, leaves me feeling more confident. Whatever setbacks arise in the future, I know I need to avoid personalizing them." Frank concludes his presentation with, "Lastly, I need to remember that nothing is really a failure if I learn from it."

"What are you going back to school for?" Alexis inquires.

"I want to be an alcohol and drug counselor."

"It's smart to go back to school, but counselors don't make much money," Alexis cautions. "I hope that's not rude to say, but I think it's the truth."

"You just need balance in all those things," John offers. "If you're too dependent on any one of them, you risk falling hard if it's taken from you. The money thing is up to you; I don't think too many people in this room love what they're doing for work, so if you find something you enjoy, just find a way to make enough money to live on now and retire comfortably later. If you want to make money, you just need to hustle and out-work other folks, and the money will come."

3/27/2013
Individual Counseling Session: 60 minutes

Frank is on time for his appointment and visibly happy as he walks into the office. In response to being asked how things are going, he grins, "I'm killing it right now. So happy."

"What's the reason for this joy?" queries Primary Counselor with a smile.

"Well, two Sundays ago I ran the Shamrock Run downtown, my first race. It was the 15k, which is the longest distance they had. It was such a cool scene with so many people choosing to get out of bed on a Sunday morning to run up a pretty tough hill. I think I heard it's the second-largest overall event on the West Coast, which seems right because there were a ton of people. There were around 7,600 runners for the 15K. I finished in 674th place—that's in the top ten percent. Last year around this time I was running, like, two or three miles, real slow, and now I'm in the top ten percent. I killed that hill, too; I was flying by people. It felt really good—now I get why people run races. It was so fun. I loved the competitiveness and the environment."

Primary Counselor observes, "You're really proud of this accomplishment."

"I am!" Frank enthuses. "I ran a lot of miles before this race. I spent so much of that time listening to podcasts and audiobooks, trying to learn and run at the same time. I accomplished my goal by continuing to get off my ass, which required that I consistently ignore the monologue in my head telling me things like, 'take today off,' and 'one day off won't hurt.' I've listened to the voices in my head tell me, 'Have a drink,' and 'You deserve it,' for so long that it's kind of amazing to see that this is what it looks and feels like when I block out the negative self-talk. These things go hand in hand, a bunch of different thoughts that want to rob me of this feeling and keep me in the muck. I also just got my grades back and I got a 4.0! First term, all As—and one class was keyboarding, which required a lot of practice—plus the time-intensive math class. I've established a good routine. I knock out my homework after James goes to bed; I just sit on my couch with my computer, with the tv on but the volume turned down. I try not to stay up later than eleven o'clock, which helps me get up and do what I need to the next morning. I'll be taking my first prerequisite for the alcohol and drug counseling program next term. I'm looking forward to that class. Because acceptance is limited, I want to see who else is looking at getting into the program. If my grades stay this good, though, I shouldn't have any problems getting accepted."

"Any triggers to use brought up by being back in school?" Primary Counselor asks.

"Just the opposite. I see some young students in my classes who are hung over or sleep deprived or whatever;

you know, just young. I was that dude, thinking I was going to be able to half-ass it with some jokes and charm. I thought I had it all figured out—wouldn't even buy the books. Now, though, I'm not young, this is costing me money, and I'm taking time away from my son. All of this, but particularly the last, mean a lot, especially considering the situation of John from group. James is sacrificing time with me and this will increase as I continue. I'm gambling that the sacrifice he's making now will be worth it in the long run, and I'll lose that bet if I half-ass this again."

"How will it be worth it to him?"

"Well," Frank answers thoughtfully, "he'll see me accomplish my dream. He'll know that if I went to college at 36, his options won't end just because he passes the traditional age to accomplish something. This shows me walking the things I'm talking. From the research I've done, I'll make more money with a degree than without one. I'll have less risk of unemployment, so when the economy goes to hell, I'll probably be less negatively affected than someone without a degree. Financial stability is so important for a kid. My son will be able to focus on what he should be concerned with at his age instead of worrying about how our basic expenses will be covered. I also think that if I'm doing something I enjoy, I'll be happier, which will make me a better parent. In addition, learning as much as I can about the disease of addiction and how to talk about it will help me talk to him about it. I know I have addiction in my family, so does his mom's side, so he may already have a propensity for it. I don't want him to follow this path, so I hope I can help him channel his pain into something other than escapist substances. I can help provide him with some tools to cope with life as it comes."

Frank's assignment, as he nears his one-year sobriety mark, is to recap his last year in treatment. He must discuss what has worked, what has been difficult, what he needs to continue working on, and the emotions he's experienced throughout the process. He will present this in the group that takes place after his one-year mark. This project is assigned to each group member as s/he reaches one year of sobriety. Frank shares that he's been looking forward to it.

4/17/2013
Group Counseling Session: 90 minutes

Nine members present for group. Frank checks into group, saying his clean date remains 4/14/2012. He shares his mood is a "nine," explaining, "I got a year clean this past Sunday." He states that his commitment to staying sober is "100 percent, even with all the things we have to do in this program, this year has been something new. And I don't want to go back. I don't know if I've ever had a great year before this, maybe some good weeks, but never a whole year." Frank announces that he has homework ready to present.

Group members warmly congratulate Frank on the milestone. "They say the second year is the hardest," Sharon comments, "but they say that about all of them! I had four years once, was doing all the things I was supposed to. Had a sponsor, was working the steps. My boyfriend at the time hurt his back and got really depressed, started drinking a lot. I started to feel guilty for leaving him to go to meetings when he was feeling so bad—he put on the pity party routine, and I fell for it. I started hanging out at home more, got complacent, got mad over money, and had a drink. That's all it took. I didn't get sober again until this program. Whatever you're doing Frank, keep doing it."

"I'm getting closer and closer to that one-year mark," Kenny shares, "It's funny that there are people who go a year without drinking and don't even notice it, but for us, a year sober is like winning the Super Bowl."

"It's because you're getting brainwashed by the AA cult," Sam interjects, "The coins are just a reinforcement intended to make you think you're weak and can't function without them; that's the reason there is so much attention to God and how you're unable to do this on your own."

"Yeah, it's a weakness to be around people who have chosen not to get wasted and are trying to improve their lives," Alexis retorts sarcastically, "I do have a weakness, it's that I think I can handle booze and keep my life straight. AA a cult—are you kidding me? Ever sat in a dive bar? How is that not a cult? You think you're so damn smart, yet you got two DUIs."

Primary Counselor attempts to interrupt Alexis, who continues, her voice rising, "I know what you're going to say, and I'm sorry, I shouldn't have made that comment. You're entitled to your opinion, Sam, but it doesn't need to be shared in a way that's disrespectful to the people who are working that specific program. So instead of dissing on other people's program, why don't you tell us the program you use to deal with your problems?"

Sam answers confidently, "I don't have a problem with alcohol."

"I'm not surprised to hear that," Alexis sighs, "there's nothing that more closely resembles brainwashing than denial, and that appears to be your recovery program."

Primary Counselor interjects, firmly this time, "I want to get the group refocused on the task, but it's important to recognize people's passion around this subject. This is a reason there's so much stigma around addiction; it's because people have different beliefs around what addiction is and how to address it. That's why we have group as a place to talk through this safely, while treating each other with respect and allowing for differing opinions. This will be something you continue to face moving forward and understanding how to process it safely will be important. Are we feeling comfortable to move on to homework?" As the group members all nod, Primary Counselor turns to Frank, "Okay, you're up."

First Year Clean Assignment

"This assignment is called *How I was brainwashed for a year!*" Frank begins. The whole room cracks up, and Frank, laughing too, needs a second to gather himself before continuing. "I'm just messing with you, Sam," he warmly assures the new group member. "It's funny, because this assignment is about how I got a year clean, and part of it is AA. I can't say I love AA, and I'm not doing it as it's meant to be done. I started AA by going to the Scully's meeting, which is known for being hardcore. People know the Big Book inside and out; it's not soft. Well, given what I know about my pride, I figured if I was going to hustle my way through this program, I needed to know that book well enough for me to talk like I was in the club. So I got it on audiobook and listened to it while I ran. The more I listened, however, the more a piece here and there would stick with me, until finally I realized I'd hustled myself. I've also scoffed at the God aspect of AA. It wasn't my thing and I was a non-believer. One day, at around three months sober, I'm sitting in a meeting, feeling really negative. I'm judging all these people who're talking about God. Then, the bracelet strapped to my leg makes the buzzing noise it makes every twenty minutes. I look down at it, and I have a moment of clarity. I think to myself, 'You could be the dumbest person in this room, and you're sitting here judging all these people.' I have a fucking breathalyzer attached to my leg, and I think I've got it all figured out. At that moment, I became open to the idea that I might not be as smart as I think I am, and maybe there's something out there I'm not aware of. I'm ok with spirituality. If I want to interpret my experiences as having spiritual meaning, I can find lots of examples of that in my life. I can also call it something else, like a coincidence, that's dismissive of it. Maybe that buzz was just a buzz, or maybe I needed some help recognizing something I hadn't been able to see. I think it's funny that this openness came in the form of negative self-talk, because I could always hear that.

"So how I got here—I became open to living life differently. I have taken many steps to change my health; I've lost 40 pounds this year and on Sunday am running my first half marathon. I still smoke, I love a Snickers and a Coke, but I go to bed on a schedule and am not as stressed as I once was. I can still get mad but also can get over it. I'm in school, am motivated to learn, and feel proud of what I'm doing. I now hold myself accountable for my own actions. I'm more present in my son's life. I'm developing friendships with people I didn't meet in a bar. I've paid off some debt and have a plan to pay off my fines. I stayed out of a relationship for over a year. I just met someone the other day—and that may end—but focusing on myself and James for a year has been awesome. Simultaneously, of course, it's also been difficult. I would get lonely, I would want to have sex. Now, though, I can see that I'm only just beginning to be someone who can even be in a relationship. I still bring a bunch of emotional and practical baggage with me. I've done the steps, I've made some amends. I try not to wrong people, and if I do, I work to find my part in the problem. I've been able to face situations, problem-solve, and get things done. In the past, I'd always put off tasks or projects, or just find myself overwhelmed by how hard or how daunting they seemed. Really, when it comes down to it, the hardest part of getting something done is getting started.

"I have felt all my emotions this past year. Before, I would've bathed those feelings—whether they were positive or negative—in the glow of Miller High Life. Now I'm suited up and I'm in the game instead of crying on the sideline. So that's been my year."

"Sorry, man," Sam apologizes, "I didn't mean to imply that what you've done this year isn't worth it or earned; you appear to be real and happy so congrats."

"It's cool, man," Frank assures Sam. "That was all the shine that's come from this year, but I know how hard it was. I know how it feels not to sleep because you're wondering how the hell you're going to pay this program's expenses; thinking about criminal things you can do just to pay for a UDS and knowing that relief from that stress is a seven-minute walk from my house. Going to free lunch at the park programs to get food to eat. I know what it's like to feel so out of place around people who have known me for years because I can't drink my insecurity away and slip into the Sandwich persona and be that funny, crazy motherfucker that I think everyone loves. I know what it feels like to try to change who I've always been. I know that not everyone is going to get that, and really, if the old me had heard you say that, I would've been so angry, because I would've wanted external affirmation of all my growth. I don't need the validation anymore; I'll be okay without it. I got three DUIs and I didn't even consider that I had an addiction or needed to rebuild my life until the last one. Sam, I hope you don't have any addiction issues because this is a hard way to learn the truth."

4/30/2013
Individual Counseling Session: 60 minutes

Frank shows up on time for his appointment. "This is my last treatment session, right?"

"Yes, this will be your last individual treatment session," agrees Primary Counselor. As you know, from this point forward, you and I will meet once a month for treatment aftercare appointments. During these sessions, we will focus on your recovery and probation requirements until you have completed DISP. DISP is scheduled to continue for two more years, but you can be released six months early if you meet the necessary criteria. You will maintain the random drug screens while in DISP. If you need additional support while in the program, you can request more sessions and can attend group at any point. After completion of DISP, you are off probation, and you and I will communicate with each other four times per year until the study is complete. Those meetings can be scheduled when you have availability."

Frank acknowledges that he understands what to expect moving forward.

Primary Counselor asks about the positive things going on in his life.

"So many things. I'm having a blast with the kids' t-ball team I'm coaching. Our name is the Wombats—get the play on words there? It's cool being Coach Frank, I like that title. And the parents are great; they help a ton.

"It's funny because to teach t-ball to little ones you have to start from the beginning, you can't take anything for granted. You introduce the game by explaining what a ball and bat are, and even what direction you run around the bases.

"I feel as though that's how my recovery has been. I've had to learn so many basic things—either all over again or for the first time—and dispel some of my life-long assumptions. Treatment has been like t-ball practice. 'This is addiction; this is what shame feels like; you can't hang out with people playing basketball and expect to play t-ball; etc.'

"I needed to be open to this information and instruction. I'd always thought I was so smart. If someone talked to me who I felt was less intelligent than I, or condescending, I wouldn't listen. I think I disguised a lot of insecurity with false pride. So working with the Wombats, my team of four- to six-years-olds, and their parents, who are very invested in their kids' wellbeing, has taught me a lot about who I want to be and the people I want to surround myself with. My son caught a flyball last week in his t-shirt—we were all trying to find out where the ball went, and it was in his shirt— the first registered out. He was so proud to make an out, he had a little swagger after that. I grew up playing football and my parents didn't have much involvement in it until I was a senior in high school. I often had to wait in parking lots to get picked up after all the other kids had left. All my friends, coaches, and teachers knew that my parents hardly bothered to show up to watch me play. I don't want to be that dad. If James grows up and has resentments about me, he is going to have to get creative—I'm not giving him parental abuse, addiction or neglect—he's going to have to think outside the box."

"I could feel your joy when you shared that story," Primary Counselor observes. "You've always had that joy when talking about your son. It only makes sense you would enjoy activities in which you get to coach him. The two of you seem to have bonded over that. You have a similar energy when you talk about school and running, which are both new activities you started when you got sober."

"I forgot to tell you that I ran that half-marathon I was talking about in group. There were 1028 runners and I took 52nd place with a time of around one hour and 32 minutes! I can't believe it. Being out there, competing with all the other runners is really exciting—I practically get a runner's high just thinking about it. I never could have predicted this happening. I didn't think I could be a good runner; I just liked the way it made me feel. Now I get to see the fruits of the work I put in, all the runs in the rain and getting out there when I'd much rather have stayed home on the couch watching Breaking Bad. I can hang with people who do fun and interesting things now, and it's because I'm doing the work.

"I can imagine what running will look like when I quit smoking, which I'm getting closer to. I've already cut down. My kid really wants me to stop, and I lie to him about it, and that doesn't feel good. I don't like putting him to bed and reading or talking to him while my thoughts are actually focused on getting downstairs so I can finally have my smoke. I know that one day—when he's too old to have daddy read him a story—I'll wish for these quiet bedtime moments with James, but right now I'm speed reading through story time. Look at John, he would do anything for that kind of time with his son, while I rush through it, preoccupied. It's gross. I'm tired of keeping secrets and having an addiction that I know is totally against everything I'm working towards. And yet it's so tough to stop. My goal is to quit by the marathon in October."

Primary Counselor asks Frank to complete his relapse prevention plan and present it to his last group. Frank acknowledges he understands the assignment.

5/15/2013
Group Counseling Session: 90 minutes

Ten members present in group. Frank checks into group, saying his clean date remains 4/14/2012. Frank shares his mood is a "ten," commenting, "I've watched so many others complete treatment, and today it's finally me." He states that his commitment to staying sober is 100 percent. "I've had so many moments this year when I wanted to have just one drink, or I'd be so pissed off about something with my son's mom, where my body felt like it was begging for a drink. But I didn't drink and instead of backtracking or staying in the same rut I had dug for myself, I took care of life as it came, and some cool things happened, most I could never have imagined. This is only the first year, and I'm just trying to stay focused so that I can continue this momentum." Frank announces that he has homework ready to present.

John checks in, saying, "My son is having some medical problems and they seem to be getting worse and I feel as though I have no control over anything. I'm terrified of him dying, and right now I'm not able to see him even close to the amount I want to because of being restricted by the mom and DHS. I'm so frustrated. When I'm actually allowed in the hospital, I must act like a robot because if I'm visibly stressed out, his mom will use that as evidence that I shouldn't be allowed to see him. I mean, it's normal to be stressed and emotional when your child isn't well, but what happens if I'm a robot? Then it comes off as though I don't care, and why should I even be there if my son can't tell that I care when I'm there? There's no risk-free façade that I can adopt in front of his mother, and all I want is to be a dad to my son. Not to mention that right now, even more than usual, he needs all the love he can get."

After a lull, Sharon affirms, "We see the good dad you are, John. I don't know if that helps, but I hope you can see it."

"Man, I'd lose it in there, Sam interjects, "Seriously, they wouldn't be telling me what to do when it comes to my kid."

Frank quickly retorts, "I don't think you can say that unless you're in his position; if he loses it on a member of his son's family, he just makes them think they're right about him. He's doing what he needs to. I bet John understands wanting to lose it more than anyone."

"I'm just sorry your baby is hurt and that you're hurting because of it," Alexis adds softly. "I hope talking about it helps."

"It does," John replies slowly, "I'm glad no one gave me advice or told me what I should do. I think I know how I need to act. The issue is keeping it together emotionally so I can."

"I got to say that watching you go through this and how you continue to cope has been the most important part of what I've taken from this group,"

Frank comments, "and you and I have talked about this outside group, about some of the similarities we have, and I just hope so much that wherever this part of your journey takes you, some happiness and stress-free times are waiting for you and your son on the other side."

After check-in concludes, Frank informs the group he will present his Relapse Prevention Plan.

Relapse Prevention Plan Assignment

Frank shares the feelings and behaviors he's identified as potential indicators he might be heading toward a relapse. "Well, I think one sign would be my feeling depressed and not wanting to keep doing the things I enjoy currently, especially running and schoolwork. Another would be my making excuses or telling lies about my failure to do something, particularly if that something involved AA meetings. My acting irritated, stressed, or angry would also be red flags. Lastly, going to places I know I shouldn't be: bars and other places that focus on booze, would alert me that I'm in danger of relapsing. I think those are my main warning signs. If I experience any of them, I know I need to take immediate action.

"Next, I wrote down my triggers. I think if anything happened to my son that would be my biggest trigger. My relationship with James' mom and her mom is another huge trigger for me. All three of us struggle to keep our focus on the present, but we end up in the same arguments we've had for years. The worst of my character defects emerge when I'm trying to communicate with them. Certain geographic areas are also triggering, like I try to avoid Alberta street in Northeast Portland because I lived on that street and drank on it for many years, and it almost killed me. I think the only other triggers are feelings of shame or depression.

"The next section names my preventive actions, which are the things that I'm doing to prevent triggers and cravings from happening. I need to keep running, quit smoking, remain on top of my schoolwork, and take some time for fun activities with James, like our planned trip to Michigan after school ends in June. I must keep my conversations with James' mom in the present and not engage in heated exchanges; maybe plan a run after a phone call to release some stress. Keep going to meetings, share my experiences and listen to others' experiences. Maybe do the steps again. Continue to observe a firm bedtime and try to eat less sugar.

"The next part is the coping skills I can use. I've used a lot of counter-thoughts this year, mostly when I've noticed I'm not thinking or behaving healthily. I often think about what I can control. I can't control other people. However, I can—often—control myself. For example, when I don't feel like doing something, I often tell myself to just get up and do it, reminding myself I'll feel better when I've completed whatever it is. I stick to routines because they've been working. I focus on the positive, and I try not to beat myself up.

"The last section lists what I need to do when I'm at risk. I can go to a meeting or for a run. I can call Primary Counselor or my case manager. I've got a few friends I can call; I've talked to John about calling him or I can call my best friend's dad who has a lot of clean time. Sometimes just going to the gym will help with stress. These are the main things I can do, but I hope to avoid getting myself to a place of risk in the first place."

The group acknowledges Frank's work in treatment.

John goes first. "I hope we keep in touch. It's been fun having you here. You were positive and brought the laughs. I wish you and your son the best."

Sharon joins in. "I agree with John. I've enjoyed you being here, it was a pleasure to get to know you. We need more fathers like you two men."

"It's been nice being able to voice some of my frustration with men and society without it being dismissed," Alexis tells Frank appreciatively. "You were a big part of letting that be heard, especially when you listened to some feedback from me, and thanked me for it, even when it might have been hard to hear. I think you could be a counselor; you're easy to talk to."

Frank thanks them all. "I will miss this group—not enough to come back—but enough. I learned a lot from everyone who sat in these seats. I laughed a lot while in group and am so appreciative that we could find that laughter during this experience. Thank you all so much!"

POST-TREATMENT

6/4/2013
Individual Counseling Session: 60 Minutes

Frank arrives on time for his session. He reports no substance use since his original clean date. He mentions that he's been experiencing some stress but reports no urges to drink alcohol. When asked what's causing the stress, Frank responds, "I've just got a lot on my plate. The Wombats finished up our season this weekend and we're having a party for the team. Coaching's been a lot of work for me, partly because there's no assistant coach. Thankfully, I've had some parents who've helped a bunch, and it's been so worth it, but I'm glad it's almost over. At our last practice, we filled up all these water balloons and had the kids practice throwing and catching them. They loved it! We have this routine where one kid gets to stand in the middle while the others gather in a circle around him and the one in the middle yells 'Who are we?' and the others yell "Wombats!' and then they all collapse on the ground. I'm going to let my son be the one in the middle for the last game. He's had to take on this commitment with me, and it means we don't get to miss practice, plus we're the first ones there and the last to leave. In addition, we're riding a bike with a tag-a-long to practice! I'm proud of him for being a trooper."

Primary Counselor asks Frank about his school status.

"I have one presentation that's due this week and a paper due in two days and then I'm done. I should keep my 4.0 GPA. The Introduction to Addiction Counseling class was interesting. The first couple classes, some of the students were acting like it was an AA or NA meeting, wanting to tell their story of recovery instead of concentrating on what we're supposed to be learning. I love a good story, but I'm not paying to hear your story, that's why I go to meetings. I'm in class trying to get a career. I think there's a bit of a weeding-out process happening—so many people get motivated by their recovery to pursue a career in counseling—but when they actually get into class, the reality of school may not match their expectations."

"Do you feel as though you're on the right path academically?"

"I have no doubt. We used Dr. Gabor Mate's *In The Realm Of Hungry Ghost* as our textbook and I couldn't believe how good it was and how much he understands this disease and the role played by the presence or absence of secure attachment to a healthy caregiver in childhood. I hadn't known what healthy versus unhealthy attachment was. The security that a baby feels when it's safe and cared for is the environment where the neurochemistry is wired for proper development. If this safety is not created this wiring is starting out with interference. I was reading it and feeling so grateful that my recovery put me in a place where I would see this book!"

"Speaking of attachment, you're close to going home for vacation," notes Primary Counselor.

"I see what you did there," smiles Frank, "reminding me of all the things I'm feeling good about—nice job. And yes, we leave on Saturday. Everything has been okayed and paid for. I'm so excited for James to meet and play with his cousins. This will be the first time my family has seen me sober since I started drinking. We're staying at my brother's and he and his wife drink, but not a lot and they understand I can't, so we won't be going to bars or anything like that. I think it could be awkward for my folks to know I'm not drinking. They may feel it calls attention to their own drinking, or they could become uncomfortable because my not drinking changes the family system. I think having all the kids together will be a good distraction, though. I plan to run a bunch while I'm there. I have a solid plan around seeing friends. I have a big group of friends I grew up and drank with. We're all doing a family pool party at one of their houses, so that way I get to see as many people as possible and can leave if I feel triggered in any way. If I feel uncomfortable, I can always jump in the pool and play with the kids. From afar, everyone has been supportive, although my mom made one kind of a weird comment, 'So you're going to AA now?' Her dad was in AA for almost thirty years, so she probably has her own thoughts about it, but I don't want to judge because it will just lead to resentments. If AA is part of a discussion, then alcoholism is indirectly part of it, so having to talk about something they've avoided for years must be uncomfortable for my parents, who have their own issues with alcohol. If anyone wants to talk about it, I can talk for days. If not, I'll just show everyone what sobriety looks and feels like through my actions alone. Either way, James will have a vacation that should provide him with some innocent childhood memories. In poker, we call that 'winner, winner, chicken dinner!'"

8/6/2013
Individual Counseling Session: 60 minutes

Frank shows up for his appointment on time and states that his clean date remains unchanged.

Asked if he has anything he wants to talk about, Frank responds, "I do have a crazy story. I've tried everything you can think of to quit smoking. I've got this marathon happening in October and I want to quit before it. A friend suggested getting hypnotized, which is something I would never have been open to in the past, but I'm desperate. So I make an appointment, which costs me about $200. I go and meet with this guy, huge tall guy, big furry mustache, looks like Magnum PI. I go into his office and we talk a long time about why I want to quit. I tell Magnum I don't enjoy it, I can't afford it, I'm lying to my son about smoking, I'm thinking about smoking when I'm playing with him or reading to him, plus I'm running a lot and training for a marathon, so it doesn't make sense. I'm also tired of having addictions; I stopped drinking so it's time to stop smoking.

So Magnum takes all this info and puts me in this comfortable dentist chair type deal and has me put on oversized headphones. He explains to me that he's going to hypnotize me to the point where he can speak directly to my unconscious mind to share with it all these reasons why I want to quit. He starts playing this like dubstep/light trance music and starts talking into the headphones. He has this big microphone that has a large black cushion over the end of it—it looks kind of ridiculous. Magnum gets me into this relaxed state and counts me down from ten really slowly. I don't remember the lower numbers, just a faint glimmer of what he was saying, but it really felt like I was out. About thirty minutes later Magnum wakes me, and it felt like the whole thing had only been a minute or two. He lets me know that I may have an urge to have a smoke, and if I feel like I must have a smoke to find the worst cigarette possible—which for me is a menthol anything—and smoke that, so it's already not enjoyable. He also tells me that when I feel a craving, I can squeeze my pointer and middle finger together to take the focus off what I'm thinking and feeling. That was a week and a half ago and I haven't had a smoke since. I haven't even felt an urge to smoke. Not sure what Magnum did in there, but, knock on wood, I think it worked."

In response to a question about why he hadn't been open to hypnotism in the past, Frank acknowledges, "It was an easy thing to be critical of, and I thought I knew everything. That's not a good combo for being open to new experiences, hence my repeating the same damaging behavior for around 20 years."

Asked how he feels about the summer ending, Frank declares, "I'm ready. James starts kindergarten at the Japanese Immersion school and I can't wait for him to start making new friends in the neighborhood. Plus, when he's in class every day, I'll have a window of time to get stuff done. I've started working in a food cart making sandwiches where I have the flexibility to work when I need to so that provides a bit of income. The owners just welcome my help and let me choose the days I work in advance and plan around that. The food is so good. It's a Philadelphia sandwich shop that doesn't actually sell Philly Cheesesteaks; instead, they've got all these other delicious things on the menu, and I get a free work meal, so that's a great perk.

"I'll mainly work when James is with his mom or grandma. I've been having the hardest time dealing with them. We're all so headstrong and believe our way is the best way. They want to revisit past conflicts and disagreements, and it feels as though their perception of the past becomes more and more distorted. I've been sober for sixteen months now and am so tired of living in that stressful place. It's so up and down; everything is cool and then it's all manic. It's hard to ride that emotional wave with them. I get all crazy and afraid of their impact on James and worry about what I can't control. I don't know—I've been looking into what it will take to have full parental custody—the instability of our arrangement is scary and it's having an impact on my ability to keep it together. Plus, the alcohol use of people in James' mom's family negatively affects him. I'm hopeful that the school will provide some structure for everyone, but I can't lie—it's stressful. The thought of it being this way for the next thirteen years is fucking crazy to me. I guess that's why they say don't future-trip. I'll tell you this, I understand what it's like when you're trying to grow and move forward and you're in a relationship with people who, due to whatever they've got going on in their own lives, can't and don't.

It makes me reflect on the fact that some of my past partners undoubtedly wanted that growth and probably blamed themselves for my unwillingness to grow with them. That's one area of so much misunderstanding around addiction—if you're in a relationship with someone in active use and you don't know anything about addiction, what are you supposed to think? You only see the decisions that person makes and you try to understand the reasons behind them. Because the addict's choices are often clearly harmful or immoral, they're baffling to those who witness them. But the addict's seemingly irrational choices make sense in the addict's world because they meet a need, such as numbing feelings by ingesting a substance or distracting them with the adrenaline one gets from physically dangerous activities. A person with addiction wants to feel well, and that feeling of wellness comes with using and/or acting out. Without the chemical or activity to obliterate the addict's feelings, he/she will generally become overwhelmed with cravings, anxiety, depression, sweats, stomach issues, and other miserable effects of physical withdrawal from an addictive substance and lack of distraction from emotional pain. If the non-addict doesn't understand this, there's no way for him/her to make sense of the addict's behavior."

Primary Counselor explores this last point by asking, "What were some of your own irritational or immoral behaviors that your past partners couldn't understand?"

Frank thinks for a moment. "My actions around money. There was no money management. Paying bills was always this chore because of the little margin I had between my income and my expenditures, i.e. my bills after the cost of my alcohol use. It must have made the other person feel stuck, unable to move forward because my lack of disposable income often meant that my partners had to pay for shit. Another thing is just the degree of my inebriation—how do you wake up next to that, seeing that as a routine practice, especially if I had pissed myself? From my partner's perspective, it must have been baffling that my experiences getting that drunk didn't make me want to change my behavior. In my mind, though, those kinds of events just supplied more shame, which I could only blot out with more alcohol."

"And if you're able to act in ways that are rational and align with your values, how would you like to behave?"

"Hmm," Frank ponders, "I think it's funny to say, but I want to be successful. I've watched most of the friends I grew up with attain at least some measure of success; they get to buy houses, maintain relationships, travel. That's what I want. Living paycheck to paycheck is a drag, it's stressful. In my past relationships, I would have liked to have grown up and been someone my partners could have been proud of instead of someone for whom they had to make excuses. I hustled some people with talk about who I wanted to be and sold them on those possibilities. I wish those could have been truths instead of lies."

10/8/2013
Individual Counseling Session: 60 Minutes

Frank shows up for his appointment on time and shares
that his clean date for alcohol remains unchanged and he
has not smoked a cigarette since being hypnotized. Frank
is walking differently from normal. When questioned, he
explains, "I ran that marathon this past Sunday. It was
humbling. I ran it in three hours and 49 minutes, which
is pretty good, but sounds better than it was. I struggled
that last six miles and got a cramp so bad that I walked
the last mile. I am so sore; I can't get over how hard
it was. I had a Rolling Stone's radio playlist going, and
when I hit the runner's wall around mile 22 and Simon
and Garfunkel's song *Bridge Over Troubled Water* started
playing, I thought I was going to die. That was not the
song for that moment. I learned I was not mentally or
physically prepared for the race. It was a cool scene,
though, with all the runners, music and excitement
about the race. I loved being someone who was running
a marathon and want to keep doing them forever. Even
though this race injury hurts, running marathons
feels like something that I was always supposed to be
doing—wish I'd found it earlier in my life, but I might
not have appreciated it as I do now. As I ran by people, I
wondered if they had stories like mine—if any of them
were recently as far away as I was from being a marathon
runner. I know I didn't invent something that will change
people's lives or anything like that, but I ran a marathon,

and that is huge for me. This pain is mine—I hobble with pride."

"It is yours and you earned it honestly; don't let yourself take anything away from your own success. It's too easy to minimize our accomplishments."

"It's funny you say that," Frank responds, nodding his head. "I had a situation this weekend where I didn't keep strong boundaries and my trust in some other people broke as a result. I got some money taken from me because I failed to protect it adequately. I'm not going to get into who did what because it just pisses me off, but I didn't take enough steps to protect some money I had and now I no longer have it. I must take responsibility for my part in this. There are some people from whom you can't expect reason and you can't reason with the unreasonable. When you try to get logic from the illogical, that's your own shit—I mean, what the fuck are you trying to reason with unreasonable people for? That's a tough lesson and I was near rage that it happened this weekend when I had this marathon, but I'm going to learn from this and move forward without letting it diminish how great I feel. In the past I would let much smaller things than this become mountains big enough to need ski lifts. I'm trying to change that. While I handle small things pretty easily now, big things still sometimes make me want to have a drink."

Primary Counselor observes that it sounds as though Frank managed to handle some difficult emotions over the weekend, accepting both the highs and lows as they came. "What are your two biggest takeaways from this weekend?"

"I learned that I can survive pain, and that you can't rely on hope—and you can't give other people access to your bank account."

11/13/2013
Individual Counseling Session: 60 Minutes

Frank shows up for his appointment on time. He shares that his clean date remains unchanged and that he has not smoked a cigarette since quitting. He also announces that he's been accepted into the Alcohol and Drug Counseling Program at Portland Community College. "It's a cohort model and our cohort will begin in the spring term this coming April," he explains. "Next year at this time I'll be doing an internship as a counselor. It's a strange thing to get my head around. Not even quite sure what a cohort is?"

Primary Counselor explains, "A cohort is a group of students who start at the same time and all move through the program at the same time. It's a good way to develop a network and friendships because you will spend a lot of time with the same group of people."

"That seems cool. I can get competitive when I'm around people who want the same things I do. I think I can come off as cocky. I hope I don't because I have no reason to be cocky. I don't know what I'm doing, so why would I be competitive?"

"Why do you think you're that way with others?" queries Primary Counselor.

"It's just a way to stay isolated, which is more comfortable than having to meet people. The cohort could help with that because it'll force me to get to know people. I need that. This is one of the reasons AA is not really for me. I know that in an hour I can just walk out the door without talking to anyone. I like to listen to people share about their experiences, but I'm still socially stunted so I just avoid the post-meeting social jam sessions. People seem to genuinely enjoy them, so I don't judge. I think it's great. I think some people are both introverts and extroverts at the same time. When I'm comfortable, I'm outspoken and social, but it takes some time for me to get there. I do think I'm getting more confident, or at least less insecure, about what others may think of me."

"What do you think about yourself?"

After pondering the question for a minute, Frank replies, "I'm trying to find that out. I'm happy, but still not comfortable in my own skin." He continues, "I just started seeing someone and she's great. She's a runner, owns a house, has a career, and has the cutest kid. And it's chill. The kids have fun playing and there's not a lot of pressure on her or me. But I've got to be upfront about a lot. I call it the 'red flag' disclosure. I have to let people know about the kinds of stuff I'm dealing with so I'm not deceiving them and they can make an informed choice about me. I had to share that I'm an alcoholic, so I won't be drinking. Also that I'm in this program, so I won't be driving for many years. I make sandwiches for income, and at 37, I'll still be in school for another five years. I have a great son who has a mom and grandmother who tend to instigate problems. And since I'm in early recovery, I kind of have to be selfish about what I need to do to stay away from triggers. I think I'm making a realistic assessment when I conclude that these disclosures don't qualify me as a catch. It's better than an alcoholic in denial, but for another adult who's accomplished many things, it's hard to sell 'at least I'm not drinking' as a big perk.

"To answer your question about what I think of me, I feel as though I'm kind of like the new medications you see commercials for on TV. They advertise some possibility of being great, and a reasonable hope of providing at least some positive effect, but at some point, there will be the disclaimer about all the potential dangers!"

"How are you at accepting these things about yourself?"

Frank pauses briefly, then observes, "I have to be ok with it, or I'll just continue to live in deception, manipulating myself into not seeing what's real, believing instead in a fantasy version of who I am and what my life is like—keeping up a façade in front of others and then allowing myself to believe in that fantasy as well. If I can recognize and accept my life as it is and then make plans around that reality, I can make progress. This also allows me to see the benefits that go along with how I'm trying to live my life now in contrast to how I lived before. My life before was so focused on my supposed deficiencies and that preoccupation led to so much depression and shame. All of the supposed benchmarks of success that I used to fixate on won't bring me the fulfillment I seek. I can see that meeting my son's emotional needs around safety and consistency is what matters most and what also fulfills my own emotional needs. This is the meaningful part of life: Raising healthy, emotionally developed children who go on to flourish in their own lives. This is what I will look back on and see as the greatest success of my life. The whole judgment of what qualities I lack as a person compared to who I 'should' be is just socialization anyway; many people in this world would do absolutely anything to be able to provide for their children the many things my son and I take for granted."

1/7/2014
Individual Counseling Session: 60 Minutes

Frank shows up for his appointment on time. He shares that his clean date remains unchanged, and he hasn't smoked a cigarette in four months. Primary Counselor asks about Frank's holidays.

"They were pretty non-eventful. James and I hung out with friends and he also spent time with some of his mom's family. I got him a new bed with space-saving drawers. I think it's cool, plus it should help with the mess—key word here being 'should.' We hung out with my friend and her daughter as well. We did this Christmas 5K run and the kids had their bikes and the event held a contest to see who had the most festive bikes and costumes. My friend dominated this contest. The kids wore costumes and their bikes had blinking Christmas lights and wrapping—they looked great. They took first and second. Her daughter took first—it wasn't even close. I told you how cute she is.

"James and I hung out on New Year's Eve, made some homemade pizza and then swiftly devoured it, something that usually consists of him eating one piece and me eating the other seven, plus we had some root beers; it was really fun. We did the countdown to midnight and threw stringers in the air to celebrate. It was really a hell of a year in retrospect. I like that I'm starting this year with goals instead of wishes. In the past, I just wished certain things would happen, but they didn't because I didn't function well enough to make shit happen. Now I have a plan for next year so looking ahead has real meaning. Different months equal different parts of my plan's timelines. If it's the norm for people to have plans and goals, it must be hard for people without addiction to understand what it's like to just hope things happen in life without planning for them. It's magical thinking that allows addicts to believe that they can make things happen; they seem oblivious of the degree to which their addiction impedes their ability to make productive changes. Try to imagine screwing up your life several times a week for years, possibly decades, and then trying to believe that this year will be different. And while other people use holidays to connect, you take that time to disconnect more, to tell yourself that you're not going to interfere with your family's holidays because they have earned their holiday and it will be better for them if you're not around.

"Sorry if that's a big answer," Frank apologizes ruefully, "I just feel different now. I went to see my family this year. I didn't embarrass myself. I think there's this unspoken thing with my brother. My family is happy with me and what I'm doing and I've put together a few good months, but he's worked hard and put together this incredible life. He has an amazing family and he's a great father. I think this positive attention I'm getting may be causing some sibling rivalry to come up. I know this is common when addicts start to get their lives together. Maybe I'm just imagining all this and it's my own insecurity about the kind of brother I've been to him. It's funny, I'd much rather have his life of doing things right and being able to drink comfortably than my current short period of positive actions/experiences. He hasn't said anything directly but we grew up around drinking so for him to watch me follow that cycle and behave selfishly in my interactions with him and his family must have been infuriating. I'd have resentments as well. I hope he shares them with me one day. All I can do is be prepared to pick up the phone on that day and listen."

2/18/2014
Individual Counseling Session: 60 Minutes

Frank shows up for his appointment on time. He shares that his clean date remains unchanged and that he has not smoked a cigarette since he quit the previous September. When asked how things have been since his last counseling appointment, Frank responds, "Things are good, I can't complain. I'm just finishing up my last requirements before starting the Alcohol and Drug Counseling program in April. Taking a human development class that explores children's developmental needs for different life stages and how a person adapts both when those needs are met and when they're not. It's incredibly interesting, especially in relation to addiction. It connects on so many levels for me right now: My own addiction, being a parent, and then starting to think about the addiction clients I'll work with in the near future."

Primary Counselor asks, "In learning about childhood development and the many potentially damaging childhood events it highlights, did anything occur to you regarding issues in your own childhood?"

Frank briefly discusses Erickson's Stages of Psychosocial Development, focusing on the stage called "Industry versus Inferiority," an evolution that in Erickson's theory occurs from ages 6-11. "Erickson's work in this stage focuses on how children begin to compare themselves to their peers. During this stage, a child's sense of competence/skill and/or of being valued in certain areas, such as schoolwork, sports, and/or family life, can help him/her develop pride and self-esteem. Children can also develop insecurities if they conclude that they do not measure up to their peers." Frank remembers that frequent earaches in his childhood necessitated the insertion of tubes into his ear canal. He recalls having some speaking difficulties around third grade for which he saw a speech teacher. "I had these issues with my ears which made me pronounce certain sounds differently from my peers. I'm sure it must have made me feel a little different. I worked on it for most of that school year with that teacher and got better, but that was followed by the less-than-stellar fourth-grade experience I told you about. After that, I moved to a new school. So between third grade and the end of fourth was a period during which I experienced a level of insecurity that negatively affected my development. Thinking about this all in retrospect, I've been able to gain a little gratitude for my mom's and stepdad's actions during this stage. They noticed this issue with my ears, brought me to doctors to get it looked at and then to get the tubes put in. They also took me to see the speech teacher. As an adult I've had a certain perspective on my childhood but reviewing these memories in light of what I'm learning helps to modify the narrative and show how much my parents did care. In many ways they were trying really hard even with the difficulties they had. It's important for me to see that." Frank continues, "Makes me think of the parent I want to be and all the moments that I care and worry that my son will never be aware of. James turned six this week. I arranged a party at an indoor trampoline park for him and all his friends, including lots of his new friends from kindergarten. My friend made him this amazing basketball cake—it was crazy—she worked pretty hard on it. Of course, at the birthday party my son's mom and grandma were dismissive toward my friend, but that's to be expected. I think there's some fear they have around other females in his life. They're just getting more and more difficult to communicate with. There's a new man in my James' mom's life, and the grandma doesn't like him, so she tries to align with me against them. I'm just so tired of being stuck in other people's triangles. If that's how you want to live, fine, but why does it have to seep into my home? It's exhausting.

"Enough about that. I'm taking a Japanese class right now. I thought it would help me connect to my kid's school. I didn't factor in how hard it would be! I'm struggling. I think there are studies on left brain versus right brain and how one of those is more adept at learning language. I think I fell and hurt that side of my head. I was sitting on my couch doing homework the other day, and I couldn't for the life of me figure out what the number 31 is in Japanese. I looked through my book and could find nothing. My son was playing basketball in the house. We have this Fisher Price hoop that he plays full imagined Portland Trailblazer seasons on. Anyway, as he's been at his immersion school for five months now where he spends half the day learning Japanese, I ask him, 'Hey, do you know what 31 is in Japanese?' After I ask, he thinks for a split second and starts singing this full, jovial song in Japanese. He's got a little dance that goes with it and does it until he gets to 31 and then tells me the answer. Seriously, the cutest thing I've ever seen, and I'm just sitting there amazed at the little brain on him. Those are the coolest moments in parenthood. There are no Facebook reminders of them, they're just things that happen in the moment that are mine to keep. Social media allows you to revisit moments you've electronically documented, but my favorite parenting memories are these small treasures. Sadly, I probably missed or forgot many of them during the first four years of his life when I was drinking—am glad that my memory is no longer impaired and I get to hold and cherish the memory of the Japanese 31 song."

4/15/2014
Individual Counseling Session: 60 Minutes

Frank shows up for his appointment on time. He shares that his clean date remains unchanged and announces happily, "I just celebrated two years!" He also relates that he hasn't smoked a cigarette since he quit the previous September.

"How does it feel to have two years clean and sober?"

"It's kind of a little bittersweet right now. Don't get me wrong, two years is incredible. I can't believe what my life looks like with just two years clean. I'm really happy about that and proud. It's also cool to know if I stay on track, I could be done with the probation program in six months. I can't even tell you how good it will feel not to have to ride the MAX here once a week just to pee in a cup. I'm so tired of it, and I can't wait to have that money in my pocket—it's roughly $160 a month—that's like getting a raise."

"So in one sense, you're experiencing some relief that the process is nearing an end?" Primary Counselor queries.

"For sure. I also just found out I'm going to get a job back at the grocery store I worked at before, not in management anymore, just working as a clerk part-time. I'll be at a different store, one by my house, and they'll work around my schedule. My boss is the friend who got my son into his preschool and hired me years ago. She's great so it should work out well. Those are some of the positive things currently going on right now."

Frank shakes his head, takes a deep breath and continues, "My roommate is a mess right now. He's lived at our place for a while and it's been great because he has a daughter, so we've just split the rent/bills down the middle. He's great with paying rent and bills, but he's been drinking in the house, in his room. That was the main rule when I told him he could move in. I'm legally not supposed to have alcohol in my house, so there could be some negative consequence for me. Plus, 'Hello, I'm in recovery, you asshole. What are you doing?' He's also trying to be sneaky, but c'mon, he isn't fooling anyone, so I don't know what I'm going to do. There are kids involved, plus I need half the rent paid, but I also need to have boundaries. I don't think I'll drink but I might beat this dude's ass which will lead to some big problems for me, and those problems might cause me to relapse. My home is a mess.

"Plus," Frank continues, "James' mom and grandma are continuing to stress everyone out. I'm getting worried and I don't know what they're capable of anymore and it's kind of freaking me out. I mean, I'm not a saint or the easiest person to deal with, so the three of us working together is just not working out. I touched base with a lawyer and told him that I'm not on the birth certificate. When James was born, his mom told me that if I wasn't on it we would have more opportunity to get assistance or having the baby at the hospital wouldn't cost anything; it was some hustle that I just played along with, thinking it would save me some money, and I didn't have the long-term vision to think, hmmm, I wonder if not being on the birth certificate could come back to bite me in the ass? I just knew I was the dad and I was there, and I would stay there, didn't think anything of it. So legally, I worry they could just take him from me. They've made some comments to me in anger over the years about my not being the father, which—I don't know—it doesn't change my love for him in any way, but if I have to go for custody it could be important, so I think I have to do a DNA test. What a drag."

"That's a lot to be going through; the stress in your home in addition to the co-parenting struggles and the custody concerns," Primary Counselor reflects. "Are you dealing with it in a healthy way?"

"I am and I'm not. I've been running miles and going to meetings but I've also been isolating. I called off the relationship that I've had these last six months, which sucks because she's great. I just feel bad for bringing anyone into this right now. She had a stressful split with her daughter's dad that she's still dealing with and to ask her to support me if things get rough isn't fair. I've also realized that there was something missing. She was everything that I wanted in a partner according to the checklist in my head; she met all the criteria I was looking for. But as I've gotten more stressed, I have this part of me that I can't talk about, because she can't relate, or at least I think she can't relate. I'm not just having a co-parenting issue. I'm having co-parenting issues that could affect my recovery from addiction, and I don't know how to be in a relationship with someone who doesn't understand the importance of that piece. I didn't know that was important to me, but I've realized it is. Maybe I haven't allowed enough discussion to happen with her so that this wouldn't be an issue for me, but with everything going on, breaking up felt like the right thing to do. I guess what I'm learning is that clean time doesn't make all your issues go away. I can feel the stress I'm going through. I'm not trying to numb it, I'm trying to take care of it, but it's real and it gets my mind racing, and that negatively affects my sleep. I just started PCC's Alcohol and Drug program and I'm feeling like a fraud because I have all this shit going on and I'm thinking everyone is smarter than I am, and that all stems from the stress, it's all related. It's nice to still have these sessions so I have a place to share this. I feel calmer now after talking to you than I have the last couple weeks."

5/20/2014
Individual Counseling Session: 60 Minutes

Frank shows up for his appointment on time. He shares his clean date from all substances remains unchanged. Primary Counselor notes, "You seemed as if you were dealing with a lot last time we met and I want to check back in with you about how things are going and how you're dealing with it."

"Well, I think the big news is that I got the DNA test done with my son and I found out that I'm not his biological father. He doesn't know yet; I think I'll wait until he's older to tell him."

"I imagine that connects to many emotions."

"Yeah, but not really," Frank semi-contradicts. "I mean, I was prepared for whatever. This isn't a caring issue, it's not an 'are-you-taking-care-of-your-responsibilities-as-a-father?' issue. It's a legal formality. Our family loves him like he's my son. I love him like he's my son. If someone wants to legally challenge that then they better be prepared because I've been part of his life since the beginning and my parental resume is getting stronger every day. I think in the grand scheme of things this will be a huge life lesson for him, as it has been for me. I needed him. He helped me get out of my own head and focus on something outside myself. It took time and mistakes, but I'm doing what needs to be done to show him how to live a life where you don't use a substance to solve or avoid your problems. I'm not mad at anyone for this, I'm grateful. I get to show him for the rest of his life how special he is, and how our bond can't be broken by some tests or whatever comes from this. It's built to last. I'm not sure what's coming down the road, but I have a feeling it may be tough. I just have to stay focused on the challenges in front of me and remember that whatever is in front of me is no reason to drink."

"I think that's a healthy place to be with news that can be difficult to hear," Primary Counselor comments. "I hear a lot of gratitude and looking for the positive in a situation. Those are strong coping skills you're displaying and when the time does come to talk to your son about all this, you can explain how those coping skills helped you stay safe in this situation."

"I really hate to think how I would have handled this if I were drinking. I would've played the victim and thought how unfair my situation was and then drunk so much that I probably would've lost control of my anger or something which could have resulted in me committing some crime or something like that. Instead of getting a three-year probation, maybe I would have gone to jail or prison. And that would have left James without me— and with an image of me drunk and aggressive—and maybe having to figure out what it means that I'm not his biological dad without being able to process it with me in person. That could've had a long-lasting developmental impact on him. Maybe now is when I was meant to find this out so my focus is not on how awful this is for me, but more on how I can best protect my son and help him build some resilience from this."

6/24/2014
Individual Counseling Session: 60 minutes

Frank arrives for his appointment on time. He shares that his clean date remains unchanged for all substances.

Asked how the end of his school term went, Frank responds, "I'm just glad it's done. It was a lot—I'm glad to have had a little break. James and I took the bus up to Seattle for a three-day weekend. We went to a Mariners game and it was Little League Appreciation Day, so we got to walk on the field prior to the game. We checked out all the sites: Pike Place Market, the Space Needle, the Museum of Pop Culture, the Seattle Aquarium, and the Gum Wall. I think that last one might have been his favorite. It was nice to reward ourselves for all the hard work we did this last couple months. We played t-ball again and I coached again. This year I had an assistant and a lot of the same families; it was fun, but combined with my son's and my own school stuff, we were busy. I started summer classes this past Monday, so it's great we were able to take a mini-vacation. I have to admit, though, that even getting away with James can be a little exhausting. He's still so little that it takes a lot of work to make sure we have a food plan and have brought everything with us we might need on each outing, so even a vacation from our usual responsibilities is a lot of work."

"It's important to take time to recharge, however you can," Primary Counselor points out. "It's funny, because as a parent, after your son's grown beyond this stage, you will really miss this time when the kids are so small and innocent and you'll feel nostalgic about these memories. At the same time, it can be really challenging when you're parenting a kid that age, especially if you're a single parent and have your child by yourself for long periods of time."

"I hear you," replies Frank, "I think we both got some needed R&R. James is going to be with his mom for the next week so I can chill out some when I'm not in class. I'm thankful that his mom and grandma are co-parenting with me; I just wish it didn't have to be so hard. I mean, I wouldn't be where I am in school at this point if I didn't have people to share parenting duties with. I know co-parenting can get a bad rap because it can be tough, but in addition to providing each parent time to accomplish things on his/her own, you know what's for real? Co-parenting is way better than no parenting!"

"What do you plan to do with that free time?" asks Primary Counselor.

Frank smiles. "My life's pretty crazy right now. I want to get rid of my roommate, who as you may remember is drinking in the house. I arranged to have a friend and her son move in instead. The drinker's not gone yet, though, so right now I stay in this big family room and James has his own room. I'm cutting that family room in half and letting this friend of mine and her son live on one side. Should help all of us financially for a while, but it'll be a busy house. The current roommate is going to have to leave; I'm just tired of living with someone who drinks.

"On a fun note, though, I've been talking with a woman I know from AA. I've had a little crush on her for over a year. She was the person who presented me with my nine-month and one-year coins when she was the secretary of my home meeting. I even heard her talk about being Ojibwe Native American in a meeting. I've never heard anyone mention the name 'Ojibwe' outside my family before, so that was crazy. In addition to being from the same Native American tribe, she's also from Michigan. Being the smooth guy that I am, I didn't really say anything to her when she mentioned it except for some lame comment like 'that's cool,' and then I walked away like a scared kid. I never had a problem talking to women while I was drinking, but my go-to line then was 'You want to go have a drink sometime?' and now that I'm sober, that's obviously not an option anymore. So I've lost my go-to line and I've been a shell ever since. I was on this online dating site over a year ago and have been off it for at least 10 months. This site had effective marketing though, so I still get occasional emails that highlight local singles, and as I'm single, I've looked at them from time to time. And I saw a pic of her, so I did some Facebook creeping and friended her. She said that she was only on that site for a day or something because of the creeps on there and then deleted her account. We've been talking for a few weeks. She has a son older than James named Alex and she has more clean time than I do. We're close in age and I feel as though we're both at a place where we know what we want. I think we may get together this week for coffee. It's funny, because we've been talking for a while and getting to know each other and I'm actually finding courtship kind of fun. Dating while drinking has little of that. In fact, I don't think you can even call it dating; more like just waking up next to people," Frank said, shaking his head. "Anyway, I'm excited to see where this goes."

7/22/2014
Individual Counseling Session: 60 minutes

Frank arrives at his session on time and shares that his clean date from all substances is unchanged.

Asked what's been going on since his last appointment, Frank reports, "I completed my second marathon last week. I ran it a little faster than the one before. I think my time last week was three hours and 40 minutes. Near the end, though, my leg tightened up and I could barely bend it so I had to walk some of the last two miles. I would like to complete one without walking, but I'm still happy that I finished."

"Congratulations," Primary Counselor smiles. "Is your son able to go to any of these races?"

"He was able to come to this race. It was on the Fourth of July and my new friend Deena brought him. Their presence meant a lot to me. At the end of the race you're tired and sore but also proud of what you just did. Having James there made it easier to focus on the fact that I had finished the race rather than on how much my calves hurt. Afterward we went to Deena's place and had a pool party and then went downtown for the fireworks. I was trying to maintain my happy face, but by then I really needed to rest so I felt a bit irritated. Also, James was on my lap as we sat on this hill watching the fireworks. He's a little guy with not a lot of anything besides bones, and his boney butt was just grinding into my sore muscles the whole time. It was rough."

"It sounds as though the new relationship is going well?"

"It is. The boys get along. They have so much fun playing with one another. It's as if they've been friends for years. We've been taking it slowly, letting the guys get to know one another. And we've been able to see each other when both the kids go to their co-parents. I've been riding my bike over to the gym right by her house at 5:30 a.m. to work out with her; that's some early relationship stuff right there," Frank laughs. "A year down the road I'd be surprised if I'm still getting up at five in the morning to ride a bike across the city, but it's fun to connect like that now. She's a very interesting person. She started this company making ghee, which I'd never even heard of."

"What is it?"

"It's clarified butter. It's used a lot in Indian cooking. I've gone with her a few times to a commercial kitchen to help her make the ghee and bottle it up so she can get it to her vendors. You know, I like how grown up this relationship feels. Getting to support her with her business goals is awesome, and I'm good at kitchen stuff. I guess I like the feeling of being someone who can help others meet their goals."

"What does she think about all this?"

"Well, I gave her the red flag disclosure—shared all the negatives of being in a relationship with me right now, didn't try to sugarcoat it. I also told her that if she's willing to invest in this stock, she's buying it at a low price. I promised that it will rise in value, but she must have faith in the market! She agreed and said something that I thought was very profound: She said that she's done a lot of work to be a healthy member of a healthy relationship, and she asked if I had done the same. I could honestly say that I have. I'm not done working on myself in this area, of course, but a healthy relationship sounds so attractive.

"I can't sit here with all good news, though. What kind of therapy session would that be?" jokes Frank, before continuing; "My son's mom is going to move to the South with her boyfriend temporarily. James will stay here with me. But she wants me to co-parent with her mom. I'm worried that I may have screwed up a month ago by telling them that James isn't biologically mine. It didn't surprise anyone. His mom recognizes our bond and is just hopeful that I won't change our father-son relationship, something I tell her over and over could never happen.

"I do have concerns, though, about how the grandma is reacting to this. She repeatedly points out that I'm not connected to James by blood and says this means that I shouldn't have any say in his parenting. It's weird, because I can have really great talks with her where we get on the same page, and then a week later she's sending me some message by email, letter, or text, telling me—in capital letters—how I have no rights. It hurts, I'm not going to lie. I just can't understand why someone who loves him wouldn't want him to have a sober father figure in his life. I think my new relationship with Deena is also a factor. His mom thinks it's good, as she wants me to have a female voice of reason, but I get the sense that the idea of my son having a positive healthy relationship with a potential stepmother, as well as the presence of a stepson in my life, is somehow threatening to his grandma. If that constitutes a threat to my James then I'm reading the wrong books on child development and well-being. I know that he's faced a great deal of change in the last few years, but at this point, I'm just trying to surround him with more love from more people. I want him to have a village of positive people in his life. I think if someone finds that threatening, they should do some soul searching to figure out why. I'm just going to stay the course, keep my son focused on childhood stuff like our plans to go camping next month, and continue to get him ready for school in the fall.

"I also need to be consistent and listen to him when he wants to talk about what he's going through. He loves his mom and grandma and he'll miss his mom when she leaves, so we have to let him share his emotions with us. I just feel this ball of stress building under my shoulder blades. Running helps. And I was looking forward to talking to you about this. I'm trying not to put all this on Deena. She doesn't deserve to start a relationship with all this stress. I just hope that the grandma and I can work together. I guess we shall see."

"I'm getting a sense that the tension between you and your son's family is increasing," Primary Counselor interjects, "and I want to remind you that this is an important time to use the support and resources you have—and—if possible, extend them. Many people in this type of situation feel some reassurance if they talk to legal counsel. The fact that this is happening when you have a partner to share the struggle with feels serendipitous."

Frank considers Primary Counselor's words before confiding, "I have mixed feelings about it. You know I feel extremely fortunate to have Deena for emotional support and someone to process all this with. She's there for me and is a stable force for James and stability is healing. I also have some guilt around bringing someone else into this. I feel my guilt is healthy, though, because it means I have a conscience—and part of my recovery is not continuing to bring stress to others by my actions."

"Deena informed you that she has done the work to be a healthy member of a healthy relationship," Primary Counselor reminds Frank. "I would take that to mean she's able to make the decision to support you and your son or to determine that this is not the most ideal situation for her recovery and for her son. She's done the work to make that decision, and if she's done so and continues to support you, you need to recognize her choice from a place of gratitude and acceptance."

8/26/2014
Individual Counseling Session: 60 minutes

Frank shows up for his appointment on time, sharing that his clean date from all substances is unchanged.

Asked about the previous month and what the upcoming end of the summer means for him, Frank relates, "This past weekend I want camping with Deena and the two boys. We went to Lost Lake. It's really beautiful and we had a great time. We rented a rowboat, and after you row out to a certain point in the lake you can see Mt. Hood reflected perfectly on the water; it's gorgeous. My grandpa once told me to find a woman who is 'camping pretty,' and Deena is definitely that! We had so much fun. We ate off the fire and played games and stayed on the lake. The boys were catching salamanders. It was cool. The guys slept in their own tent, which was new for everyone. When you're a single parent you always sleep with your kid. They handled it like bosses and were so cute, just gossiping in the tent by themselves. It was so energizing to get out of town, and it was our first real adventure together. I'm super happy how well it turned out.

"Oohh, and," Frank says suddenly, changing the subject, "I also have cool news. So yesterday, the day we got back from camping, I had an interview for a job as an Alcohol and Drug Counselor for my practicum. I interviewed with this Native American treatment provider. They called me back this morning and offered me the position. I start next month. It's an outpatient clinic.

"I can't believe I get to start doing the work. I'll be at the clinic about sixteen hours per week from September until late March. The hard part will be not getting paid during that time. Money's so tight right now. That's why I moved that friend in to help with bills. My drinking roommate moved out, which is good, but I'd thought we would have a small window before he left when he, the new roommate and I would all be splitting the bills three ways. In my current financial state a third is significantly more manageable than a half. I'll be working around 22 hours a week in the grocery store and a couple nights in the food cart, but that's not enough to pay the bills. As usual, I'm stretching my financial aid payment pretty thin. With the continued cost of this DISP I'm barely keeping my head above water financially. I don't have any in-case-shit-happens money. Even if I were only making ten dollars per hour, those 16 hours of internship time would give me about $500 take home per month. I could use that but I need to prioritize getting counseling experience and you get that through internships. I wish they were paid, but as you know, in our field they aren't. But I got a really good vibe from this Native American treatment place. I haven't had much exposure to the Native American side of my family. We never really talked about it when I was growing up and I always felt that was a loss. But I could feel something when I was at this place. I interviewed for another place that I think would also have been great, but the connection to the Native American community was too good to pass up."

"It was around two years ago that you decided you wanted to become a counselor," Primary Counselor observes, "and you're now only a month away from getting to share a healing space and your growing expertise with people who are seeking help with their substance use. This is a great demonstration that a lot can happen in a short amount of time!"

"That's the exact message I hope others will receive and think about," Frank replies.

10/7/2014
Individual Counseling Session: 60 minutes

Frank shows up for his appointment on time. He appears tired, possibly stressed, but shares that his clean time remains unchanged for all substances.

Asked if he has anything to process, Frank replies, "Well…where to start…a lot has happened. Deena and Alex live with me now. Her apartment's lease was up and her brother, who had been living with her, moved back to Michigan. She was in a tough spot financially. We started discussing it and decided to try out living together; it really was getting hard to go back to our own places after hanging out all day. I talked to my roommate and she understood—she was only supposed to be at my place for a short time anyway, until she could get back on her feet. She was able to find another place to live with her son. I felt bad asking them to leave. I didn't see this happening this quickly and have worried that we're making a mistake moving the boys in together after such a short time, but they're close and we both want our kids to have another kid to play with and to be a kid with. I'm also confident we have something that's strong and can last, and we'd like to start building a future sooner than later. We might not have chosen it to be this soon in other circumstances, but this is the situation that was presented to us. We understand the dangers of moving this fast and that's why we need to work together to offset them.

"So the house I've lived in for almost six years now has gotten an upgrade. We totally had a bachelor pad. You can tell that's no longer the case and I've actually been pretty pissed off about a lot of the changes. Change is hard for me. I get defensive. It has to do with my history of shame. I take things personally. I've been experiencing Deena making changes in my home as criticism or reflecting deficiencies of my character, so it's been tough having my things replaced with other things, even if they're much nicer."

Primary Counselor observes, "From the way you're sharing this, I can see that you've both thought about the impact of your moving in together on everyone. There are opportunities here but also concerns about moving in after a few months. You seem aware of the choice you've made and that you need to be vigilant to ensure your kids are taken care of in case something unforeseen happens, like you decide living with one another isn't working and the boys get separated. What else is going on?"

"I also started my practicum. I think it's going well. I'm shadowing a couple of the woman I work with. They're both smart and solid counselors. I ask them a lot of questions and they're really helpful, even though they're very busy, as is everyone there. Most of these counselors have 35-45 people on their caseload and our agency is short-staffed. One of the counselors said they're always short-staffed because the agency doesn't pay much. I know social services are underfunded but this situation is bad for everybody.

"Next week I'm scheduled, for the first time, to facilitate a group by myself. I'm totally nervous. After that I'll be facilitating groups regularly and will also start counseling patients individually. I'll be working with patients at an Intensive Outpatient level of care, which means that they're the level right below those who need residential care—well, I guess you know that—duh.

"They do a few things I think are so cool. They have Native Drumming around lunch time. I love hearing that while I'm working, it gets me fired up! They also have a graduation ceremony on the last Thursday of each month for those who've successfully completed inpatient treatment. Clients graduate when they've met the treatment goals that were set by the staff and client together at the beginning of each client's treatment period. Patients' families, the counselors and their peers in treatment can attend the graduation and can share about the person graduating. This is cool to witness, especially seeing the families or partners talk about the person graduating. There's so much pride and hope in that moment! Each graduate gets a certificate, a feather and a coin and gives a speech. I got to see this during my first week. It was amazing. Plus, they had a bunch of food. I was told it's always this way; when Native Americans have a ceremony, you can bet there will be some great food. The whole scene was very affirming.

"Although I feel incredibly enthusiastic about the place, right now I'm just the new white guy and I know I'll need to build trust with everyone there. I've been told that once they see your spirit is a healing one, you'll be accepted. I've just got to keep being myself, be willing to learn and grow."

"Do you feel that this has helped you connect to your Native American heritage?"

Frank thinks for a moment. "I feel something, but don't know if it's the Native American link or just my finally getting to do the work of counseling people, but I feel connected to something. Continuing to come into work radiating positive energy is becoming a challenge, though," Frank continues. "My son's mom is still out of town and co-parenting with Grandma has become a nightmare. She has this Power of Attorney that the mom signed before she left. The grandma is going crazy with this, talking to the school, talking to doctors. She's trying to control everything relating to James and it's pushing my stress level through the roof. There's no communicating with her. I think she's triggered by Deena moving in—that she fears on some level that Deena and I might try to push her and James' mom out of his life. I would never do that to my child, but no one is hearing that. I feel that it's escalating, that there are now a string of manufactured crises that need daily intervention. I'm worried about how this is affecting James. He's already away from his mom and now he has deal with this drama.

"Plus, Deena has to deal with it, and she has to protect her son, so she's having to be momma bear, which is what a good mom should be doing. This is all happening at the same time I'm starting work as a counselor and I'm not making any money. It's tough. It feels like too much for everyone. I'm at a loss as to how surrounding a child with more people who care about him can somehow be a bad thing, and how isolating him from the one parent who's actually present could seem healthy, but that's what the fuck I'm dealing with."

11/18/2014
Individual Counseling Session: 60 minutes

Frank shows up for his appointment on time, reporting that his clean date for all substances is unchanged.

Frank is due to complete, or "graduate from," the DISP program the following week. He will be granted a six-month early release due to meeting all the requirements of his probation and conducting himself in a responsible, rehabilitated manner. Primary Counselor reiterates that after the graduation, Frank will no longer need to follow the probation guidelines. This means: No more UDS, no more case manager meetings, no more Enhanced Bench probation monthly court payments, no more meetings with the judges, and no more required AA meeting attendance verification signatures.

Although his probation will be over, for the sake of the study Frank will continue to attend individual counseling sessions four times per year. Primary Counselor emphasizes that if he needs more support, he can schedule an extra appointment at any time.

Asked about his thoughts and feelings as he reaches the completion of his probation, Frank considers briefly. "Life is stealing this moment," he muses. "The end of probation should be a cause for celebration, and I'm so happy and proud but in other ways this is kind of scary. I'm so grateful to know that I won't have to call that damn phone number every night to find out if I have to come here and take a UDS the next day. For that alone, today is a great day. I'm relieved to know I'll have more time and money, both of which I sorely need. Plus, I did it! I mean, when I agreed to do this, when I was just a few days sober and had to look ahead to all three years of this program in front of me, there was a huge part of me that didn't know if I could do it. I mean, seriously, I couldn't envision the not-drinking-for-three-years part, let alone all the other things that came with it. It's hard to fathom that it will be in my rear-view mirror soon.

Primary Counselor gently stops Frank to make a request. "Can you just sit in that for a moment? From your body language and what you've shared in the past, it feels as if there's about to be a 'but' to all of that. Let's pause before that, just sit here in this space. You don't need to say anything; just breathe and think that you did it; you completed this and you earned all of those positive changes. Sit in it for thirty seconds with me."

Frank sits, thinking and taking deep breaths. After a full minute, he begins to talk more emotionally. He shares that he's not had much opportunity to enjoy this success. He also acknowledges, "The other side of this is how scary things feel right now. I'm over having to come here and give UDS and have my slip signed in AA meetings, but it's kept me accountable. I mean, during the last two and a half years, if I wanted a drink, I knew that having one would mean I'd relapsed and ruined my track record. But in addition, I knew that if I had a random UDS the next day I'd have screwed up my place in this program. I'm getting out early because the probation department has documented my reliability and my commitment to sobriety. But now, it's just me. I mean, I have positive people and lots of motivation to keep going, but I'm off paper and no longer accountable to, nor under the scrutiny of, Multnomah County. And of course, is my life going perfectly right now as I start this next part of my life? Shit, no. I'm the most stressed out that I've been since my first few months of this program when I was drowning in its fees.

"My relationship with the grandma is the worst it's been. Deena and I have a meeting with a police officer to look into a restraining order against her or get some guidance on another way to handle her because I can't do this much longer. The grandma doesn't want my son to come to the DISP graduation because she doesn't think it's appropriate for a kid to see that. I think that's weird; I mean, he's graduating as well—he was my partner in this. He's been my biggest supporter. He is my reason, my heart to do this. All these months, we've had to take the bus to come to the office or go downtown when neither of us wanted to. He was a trooper, and it just hurts that he doesn't get to see his dad graduate from this. This whole thing is adding so much stress to my relationship. I think if we weren't living together, I would end it with Deena just to keep her and Alex from having to deal with this. It's not good for them and I can feel the impact it has on her because it comes back to me. And this is not a knock on her. She's been verbally attacked and the grandma has made judgments about her character that are baseless and fucking harmful. It's been triggering and increased our anxiety levels. Of course it's going to affect us; we're both in recovery because of our own issues that are triggered by stress, and now we're in permanent fight or flight mode.

"As soon as I get home, I feel an iciness radiating from her. It's seriously just five months into the relationship, and . . . well . . . we're struggling. We're taking out our anger and fear about all of this on each other. I just feel bad about how my history is still negatively affecting people I care about. I want that healthy life, but shit, the fact that everything is out of my control makes me feel unhealthy and anxious. When my phone vibrates in my pocket, I lock up. I'm terrified to know what's coming next, plus I don't want Deena to also be triggered. I can't sleep. All I do is worry. You know, there's a high likelihood that the day I graduate from this probation will be the day that I'm the most stressed out and most vulnerable to relapse."

POST–PROBATION

1/27/2015
Individual Counseling Session: 60 minutes

After requesting an individual session three weeks prior to his first planned quarterly meeting with Primary Counselor, Frank shows up for his appointment on time. He shares that his clean time hasn't changed.

Primary Counselor commends Frank for scheduling a supplemental counseling session.

When asked what prompted him to request the extra session, Frank responds, "Oh man, just thought it couldn't hurt. I can't believe it's only been a few months, but things kind of came to a head shortly after our last session. I don't even know where to start.

"My son has been living with his grandma since the end of November. We met with the police to find out what we could do because we couldn't take the threats any longer. We were told there was no real legal recourse besides going to family court and trying to get guardianship or custody. They said that in the meantime, our best option was to institute boundaries in our interactions with the grandma, as it's our co-parenting arrangement with her that's provided her with opportunities to make threats and create other drama. In short, to avoid being subject to the craziness, we needed to hire legal help or end the co-parenting relationship.

"So I gave the grandma what she wanted. I sent an email to her and the mom saying that James would be staying with the grandma and that I would not participate in this drama any longer. I would not be communicating again until it came from my lawyer. I blocked them from my email and phone. I told the school what was going on. I talked to my son and just told him it would be a while until I saw him again, but I promised it was to allow me to work on getting him back to our home the right way. That was the hardest conversation I've ever had. I also communicated with the mom's sister and the mom's dad and stepmom, all of whom are supportive and understand how much being James' dad means to me. Then I had to set the boundary and allow the grandma to have my son and no longer communicate with either of them.

"I've been a mess; just an emotional basket case. I've been breaking down at home, at my practicum, and a lot when I'm by myself. I just worry so much—wondering how he's doing, how he's coping, what they're saying to him—my thoughts are going crazy. I'm living in a state of thinking the worst. I heard his mom moved back around

Christmas, so at least he has one parent with him. That's helped me cope but I still can't get it together. I didn't see him or talk to him on Christmas. I can't even tell you how hard that was.

"Separately and in addition, Deena and Alex are having to deal with this. They can tell I'm depressed, and I feel this pressure to keep up a façade for them that I'm doing well. Which means I'm feeling guilty about my effect on everyone I love all at once. I just want to lie in a dark room with the covers over my head, which is a sign of my depression and a warning sign for relapse. I want to go away. I've been having thoughts of not wanting to be around. I haven't told anyone this, but last week I stopped at a bar I'd never been to before and ordered a beer and a shot, and just sat there. I sat there for 20 minutes, looking at it and thinking. It didn't smell good, and the place felt even darker than I felt. I just wanted to escape the worry and the guilt, but I finally thought about how this isn't fair to James—he's having to cope with this—as are Deena and Alex, and I'm thinking about drinking. I walked out, but I was so fucking close."

"This is a lot to deal with and it's challenging to all the people involved," Primary Counselor affirms. You showed great awareness in noticing the smell and the absence of light in the environment and recalling in that moment what those close to you are having to cope with. Focus on the skills you used and not on the closeness to relapse. Alcohol is part of our society, and its availability means relapse can happen at any time.

Identifying and understanding the skills you used when it was most difficult will be important so that you have those skills at your disposal. You can reinforce how to cope by remembering situations where you were at risk, thinking about how you felt and the thoughts you were having, and then considering what you did to deal with those triggers and why your response was effective. This understanding of the links between the emotional and rational parts of your brain is key for long-term sobriety.

"Separately," Primary Counselor pauses, shifting topics, "have you been able to connect with your son at all?"

"Yes. In early December we got a dog. That's what the boys wanted for Christmas. I think I had some unrealistic hopes that James would be back by then, not really knowing how the court process goes. So we got a Mini-Australian Shepherd named Chuck. He's just a puppy. We really wanted to have something that tied us all together and Chuck belongs to all four of us.

"Now, I will say this. When in a stressful, depressive crisis, I wouldn't recommend getting a puppy! Puppies are maddening: The training and the late nights. I'm already stressed out so the slightest thing that goes wrong sends my frustration and anger through the roof. The fact that I thought adopting a dog would be a good idea clearly demonstrates the degree of my brain's (lack of) clarity right now. Oh my God—it's been torture—such frustration. But then he's also the cutest thing you've ever seen. Cars literally stop and people get out just to say hi to him!

"Well, a few weeks ago after James' school started again, I went to his school about the time he got done. I wanted to see him and hug him and show him Chuck. It was so good to connect and tell him I'm working on his living situation and that soon we'll be able to see each other more and that Chuck would be waiting for him. The grandma was not happy with me, but just for a minute, I felt there was some healing."

"I can see how important that brief exchange was to you," observes Primary Counselor. "What actions have you taken to resolve this situation?"

"Well, we're making some progress. I found a lawyer who works on a sliding scale and would cost around 60 dollars per hour. I made a GoFundMe page telling my people about my current situation. I told them that I currently don't work enough to be able to cover the court costs. It was humbling to ask for money, but I needed it, and I know a lot of people care about my son. I asked for $2,500; within three days we had over $3,000! I can't even begin to tell you how it felt to have people reach out like that. Many also shared emotional support. So much positivity came our way, it was just inspiring and empowering. Ran into a speedbump shortly after this, though. Apparently, there was a conflict of interest with the legal clinic, so I had to find a new lawyer. I found one I like, but she costs $100 per hour, so it's good to have the money but it's going to go quickly. Our lawyer seems like she's worth it. We call her Brittany the Ass-Kicker!

"We scheduled a meeting with a mediator and all parties. It actually worked out well. We came to an agreement on times that I would be able to see James. It's like every other Sunday for four hours. There are some rules: I can't refer to myself as his dad, he can't go to the house he grew up in, and he can't see Deena and Alex. If that doesn't show control issues, I don't know what does. But I don't care; I'd call myself Sea Biscuit if it meant I could be with him.

"I had my first visit a few Sundays ago. We went to a community center and played basketball and had lunch and talked. He's so resilient. He's confused but he's doing ok. Thank God for his school with its structure and friendships. The grandma got him into counseling, something for which I'm so grateful. My hat is off to her for that, and his having opportunities to talk about the visitation/custody drama seems to be helping. I wish the level of caring and awareness that led grandma to put him in counseling could help her and his mother recognize that I'm also important to his well-being, but so far it hasn't. My lawyer thinks that the best move right now is just to try to get guardianship and continue to co-parent. If I try to take James away from them it doesn't align with his best interests, but with guardianship I will have more control and the threats will have no power. That's all I want. I don't want them out of his life. I would never want that because it would negatively affect him—

he would have less love. I want all the adults in his life to be able to work together, but I'm not going to just hope. I'm going to get it legalized. I'm hoping we'll have a court date in February but it may not be 'till March. It's better now that I can see him, but I miss him for the rest of the hours of the week and I'm worried about him almost all day, every day."

"You've done a lot in a short amount of time," Primary Counselor reflects. "For someone who's experiencing depression, you're really taking opposite action by working on seeing him and preparing for legal proceedings. How is this affecting other areas in your life?"

"There've been some positive things, kind of. I was offered and accepted a counseling job at the place where I'm doing my practicum. It's cool because now I'm a paid intern. It's reassuring that they reached out to me and asked me to apply; the people I work with directly seem to think pretty highly of me. I like to joke with people that I think I'm good at my job, but I don't have a lot of supervision so whether I actually am or not is really a mystery to me. I think that since it seems like I am a good counselor it's easy for managers to justify not providing adequate supervision because they're busy. Has that been your experience in the field?"

"Yes, it's true, unfortunately, that this is the norm in many places," confirms Primary Counselor. "Many treatment providers struggle with scarcity. They're understaffed because they don't have the assets to pay a livable income, so they have limited resources for deep training and supervision and they suffer from high staff turnover rates. In many places, the staff members who work with those struggling the most with addiction are those employees who have the least amount of training and make the lowest salary. Many supervisors don't have the bandwidth to fully evaluate their team members' performances."

"That's exactly what's happening here. When I got offered the job, the pay was 13 dollars per hour. In order to accept it, I had to quit a job in a grocery store where I made more and had way better benefits. I wanted work that aligned with my career goals but that's required taking a pay cut—from a job making sandwiches! It's a tough sell for Deena. I'm supposed to be going to school to make money, to provide. All I'm providing her with right now is an excuse to leave my sorry ass. She hasn't said it, but I'm sure she's having thoughts around 'that stock market is close to crashing, college boy!'

"I have to start here, though. I need the experience and my resume needs some stuff on it besides my name. It's stressful to make so little money but it won't stay like this forever. I'm not planning to be this poor for the rest of my life. Shit, I didn't get sober to live paycheck to paycheck.

"I think we're going to do some couples counseling when my benefits kick in," Frank continues. "Deena's been asking for it for a while and she's right, we do need something. My pride and defensiveness don't seem to be helping me. It's the stress of this situation; we could just use an outside voice to help us figure out how not to take it out on one another. If it weren't for our boys we probably wouldn't do counseling in a seven-month-old relationship, we'd just get out. But we made a pact with each other that neither of us would raise the subject of leaving.

"We've both been runners in our past relationships—people who start planning our getaways as soon as we get uncomfortable—and that doesn't help us problem-solve or communicate. Shit, I've already got places to live picked out in preparation for the inevitable point in the future when I would get angry with Deena. That's how I've always been and that's why I've always contributed negatively to my romantic relationships. Maybe counseling will help me learn how to be less defensive and to refrain from compulsively planning my new single life. It's helped knowing we can't go there. I get so angry thinking about how I can't fantasize about running away, but it works because then I have to start thinking about what to do next to support the relationship."

"I think that any couple who has gone through what you both have in the last few months would experience conflict," comments Primary Counselor, "and the fact that neither one of you has left the other—or used alcohol to cope with the stress—and that you're thinking about counseling, shows how important this relationship is.

Even though it's challenging, you're both using healthy relationship strategies that can form the foundation of a strong, lasting partnership."

"Thanks," Frank acknowledges the compliment. "It's hard to see when you're dealing with strong emotions, but what you say helps me view this in a different light. I've been coping by running more miles and taking on projects. After listening to different podcasts for the last year, for instance, I'm starting my own about addiction and social services. It seems like a cool project. I have a lot to learn, but I like the task-oriented part of it, plus it's creative. I'm going to interview people about different topics. I'll definitely keep you up to date on the progress.

"I'm trying to think if there's anything else going on right now. Not really. . .I'm moving right along in school. I get my Associates Degree in June. Oh yeah—going to apply to Portland State University's Bachelor of Social Work program. It would start next fall. From what I've gathered from talking with people, it's a solid program. It's also conveniently located right downtown. I can take the MAX there, so I don't have to worry about parking or spend hours riding around on the bus, plus it'll be close to my work. I hear admission to the program is competitive, so I'm a little worried, but I've done well: My GPA is ridiculously good and I'll also have experience from this job, which is one of the things they look for. My nature is to doubt myself but if I keep on track with what I'm doing, I think I'll deserve it if they accept me, and if not, it would be their loss, as I believe I would be successful there.

"But that's all stuff that's a bit in the future. I've just got to focus on what I need to do this next week, keep concentrating on getting James home and try not to relapse or lose my relationship … shit … more realistically, try not to lose my mind."

4/14/2015
Individual Counseling Session: 60 minutes

Frank shows up for his appointment on time. He states his clean date from all substances is unchanged and announces, "Today is my three-year sobriety anniversary. It's beyond words how much my life has changed in three years. I want to say thanks for all the help; I've learned a ton from group and these sessions."

"You're welcome," Primary Counselor replies, "but as you will learn as you continue in your career, seeing positive changes in a client is all the thanks a counselor needs. If you're a counselor and that doesn't fill you up, you may be doing the wrong job. So," Primary Counselor pivots to a question, "lots was going on last time we talked. What's new? How are you?"

"I'm way better, actually. It's no surprise that life can change so much in three years because it changes so much just between these quarterly sessions. Well, I'm very happy to tell you that my son is home!"

"Congrats Frank, that's wonderful news," declares Primary Counselor warmly, "I honestly feel relief for you."

"Thank you. I feel as though I've been carrying a 50-pound backpack of stress for six months and I've finally been able to let it go. Still not perfect, but I was granted guardianship of him, so hopefully the worst is behind us. The whole court scene was ultimately unnecessary. On the morning of the hearing, the grandma decided not to file her guardianship request because she realized she was going to lose, so we made a deal that allows her to see him. As I've said from the beginning, I have no problem with that. Then, suddenly, his mom didn't want to agree—said she thought I shouldn't have rights to him. I guess I'm not meant to understand how she thinks that would benefit our son. I ended up going up against his mom instead of the grandma. James' lawyer, who is court appointed, met with everyone, including James. He recommended that the judge appoint me as the guardian and the judge agreed.

"We'll have to go back in a few months, as this is a temporary ruling. The judge will allow time for more testimony at the next hearing and then choose to continue the guardianship as is or make changes. This is great and what I was hoping for. Unfortunately, another trial means another three months of my $100-per-hour lawyer. I make 13 dollars per hour. That GoFundMe money went so fast, it seemed as though it just paid for the initial handshake. I'm so broke I can't sleep. I'm so happy he's home, but I'm having trouble being present and not irritable because of my intense financial stress. It's like a gratitude exercise: I want to stay in a place of gratitude, but it's hard. Deena and I went to his school right after the trial and talked to the principal—we had already talked to her a few days before the hearing to give her a heads up. She called James in, and we told him that he would be coming home after school. He was funny. He had thought he was getting into trouble because he had to go to the principal's office! I'm so proud of him for trusting that when I told him that I was working on getting this done right, that I was, and now it is. We got to bring him home and Deena went to pick up Alex and we surprised him by James jumping out from behind the front door. It was the first time they'd seen each other in four months, which is so long for kids. There's been a lot of positive energy between the four of us, and the reunification has helped my relationship with Deena."

"Were you able to do couples counseling?" asks Primary Counselor.

"We've been going and it's helped us to learn some better methods of communication. I don't know why I felt hesitant about getting counseling. I think I believed it would bring up the idea in our minds that we had failed, or, alternatively, I told myself that we didn't need counseling because everyone has hard times. I think I just irrationally believed that since our relationship doesn't include alcohol it should be able to fix itself. My past relationships obviously had both excessive drinking and me as common factors, and I guess once I got sober, I blamed most of my prior relationship issues on the booze. It turns out that some of the problems could have been me and not the alcohol. Talking through our struggles with another person who's not emotionally invested has allowed us both to see our own parts in our difficulties and to recognize that what we've gone through has been difficult on everyone individually as well as on the relationship. Just having someone else validate our experience was helpful. It feels as though we're getting back to being more united, which I think was both of our goals for counseling, so it's been working."

"Every relationship will need some repair from time to time," Primary Counselor says gently, "it's helpful to have a good mechanic. What else is going on?"

"I started my last term at community college. Am still waiting to hear whether I'll be going to Portland State next year; I should know next month. Still trying to run as much as I can whenever I can. I keep running gear with me wherever I go, just in case, and I have a shower I can use at work so I often run on my lunch breaks.

"I've also been hosting the podcast I'd told you about. It's called *Cause and Solution,* which is a reference to Homer Simpson saying that alcohol is the cause of, and solution to, all of life's problems. It's fun. I've been knocking out an episode a week. I find someone to interview—a friend in recovery or someone who works in a social services field—then I learn about what that person does so I can have questions prepared. I interview him or her, then edit the recording and publish onto Soundcloud. It takes a lot of work and it doesn't pay anything, but I love the feeling of getting it done and published and knowing that I'm problem-solving as I go. It provides a nice relief from the stress of everything, just to have that to focus on each week. I used to get an idea to do something when I was drinking and then wouldn't start it or even attempt to. This podcast has been something completely new to me and I keep at it, trying to learn what the hell I'm doing. I may be using it to distract myself from my current financial stress. But when I get bummed or stressed out, I just look around and see James playing with Alex and our dog and it makes it all worth it."

7/14/2015
Individual Counseling Session: 60 minutes

Frank shows up for his appointment on time, affirming that his clean date from all substances is unchanged.

"I know the last time we talked you had some things happening with court and school," Primary Counselor recalls. "How are things going?"

Frank answers with a sigh, "We had the second trial and the judge ordered that the guardianship stay as it is, so I remain James' guardian. It was a shit-show. The trial's sole objective was to determine if my guardianship should continue or not. The only thing that could have changed the judge's decision to grant me guardianship would have been someone presenting evidence that I wasn't the best choice. But some people used the hearing as a platform to try to impress upon the judge how great they are. It really didn't derail the hearing because the judge kept redirecting to the business at hand, but it was hard to watch. I had thought that after the hearing I'd walk out with pride or a huge sense of relief, but although I did feel some relief, mostly I just felt really sad that it had come to that. In the course of my work now I can see the effects that people's mental health issues have on their families. And the people who have these issues usually went through trauma as a child. I see it here so much. One person is not willing or able to address the problems that have been affecting his or her family for decades, and the generational and social harm it does to those who fail to, or can't, enforce protective boundaries against the resulting dysfunctional behavior is intense. I believe that humans are connected by energy, and that disordered energy can manifest in destructive behaviors. This can cause a generational cycle of dysfunction until either the person seeks help or people protect themselves from that energy. As I say, it's sad. I hope that all of us can heal from this. We all need it.

"We still have this sweet, smart seven-year-old whose life will improve as a direct result of how far we, both as individuals and as a group, heal. Won't be easy; there's lots of resentment and damage, but we only get one chance to give him a great childhood and it's ticking away day by day."

Frank pauses to collect himself, then continues, "You know, another thing that happened during this process is that my parents have been emotionally supportive; really listening to me and showing empathy. Even my real dad has put forth some effort to be there for me, which I've found healing in some ways. I've carried so many resentments surrounding his absence during my childhood. I always had this hope that my dad would move back to Michigan from California and be the dad of my imagination. Of course he didn't, and all I was left feeling was let down. But his recent support has shifted my perspective some. You know, maybe I didn't need my dad when I was five or nine or 16 as much as I always thought I did. And we still don't have the ideal relationship I've pictured in my head all these years—throwing the football, talking about girls, him teaching me about life—I don't have that. But when I was 39 and I was going through something terrible, he was there. He listened and he cared, just like my mom and stepdad. It's made me realize that you're never done parenting. Lots of people are out there sitting in shame because they may not have been the parents they wanted to be, but every day's another chance and it's up to them to figure out who they're going to be."

"I can see the relief in you," Primary Counselor observes. "It's been an emotional year. I'm glad to see you focusing on healing and moving forward. Turning resentments into understanding, even in the cases of people who make life hard sometimes, is important self-care. As you know, resentments hurt the person holding them rather than those at whom they're directed. Speaking of moving forward, was there a graduation from community college?"

Frank confirms with a smile, "Yeah, I'm done with community college. I like to discount it as being 'just' community college, but I started community college in 1999. Then I took a long break to binge. I guess given that, my going back and finishing is kind of a big deal! Best part is I got into Portland State University and will start the Social Work program in September. Next rung on the ladder. I feel nervous. I've done well so far, but this is college for real. There will be some talented people around me and I admit I've got some doubts creeping in.

"I'll have to do another internship—a field placement—my senior year. That's 16 hours a week I can't make money. If I'm in the same financial boat I'm in now, I will sink. I've got to find a job that pays better. I can't live on this wage. I analyze and critique everything we buy in my head. It's not who I want to be but that's how it is when your bank account is busted. I don't know where I'm going to find a job that pays better with my limited experience but I'm going to keep looking."

10/6/2015
Individual Counseling Session: 60 minutes

Frank shows up for his appointment on time. He shares that his clean date from all substances remains unchanged. Primary Counselor notices that Frank is wearing a Portland Marathon 2015 finishers shirt that indicates that he participated in the race two days before.

When asked how it went, Frank declares, "It was my best race yet! This is the best shape I've been in in years and it showed. I ran the Hood to Coast relay race last month for the first time. My team was totally made up of runners in recovery and our name was One Leg at a Time! The difficulty of each leg of the race is ranked and the one I ran was the hardest because it included some big hills. I killed it. I can't remember ever feeling that ready for anything physical. I was in good shape in the Army but still drinking and doing drugs. When I was running, I felt as though I was floating.

"The confidence I gained from last month's race definitely carried over to this marathon. I ran it in three hours and 24 minutes. This is my fastest time and almost 12 minutes faster than last year. It makes me feel optimistic that I could qualify for the Boston Marathon. At my age that requires a run time of three hours and 15 minutes. I'm like nine minutes away from qualifying. So cool to be that close, but shaving off those last nine minutes will be difficult, especially with starting school again."

"I'm not surprised at all about your running accomplishments at this point," Primary Counselor comments. "Your feelings about it have always sounded like love. How has your transition been to Portland State?"

"I'm loving my classes so far. I'm surprised and fascinated by some of the subject areas that are important in social work. I have an Oppression and Privilege class that's eye-opening. Learning about micro, mezzo, and macro oppression within the context of the social issues that affect the folks I'm working with will allow me to be more open to hearing about, as well as better able to understand, the obstacles they face when trying to improve their lives. I think that anything that helps me to more fully empathize with my clients will make me a better counselor.

"I'm also learning about my own privilege. I mean, I'm the definition of privilege: I'm white, straight, cisgender, male, and able-bodied. The only elements I'm really missing are the upper-class socioeconomic background and the Christianity. I'm starting to think about some of my most significant experiences with my privilege in mind. It seems it may have manifested in ways I would never have considered."

"Tell me more," urges Primary Counselor.

"Well, it's interesting. You know, I can remember that through the most challenging and desperate times in my life—the periods of heavy drinking and depression, the suicidal ideation and attempts, the legal consequences of my behaviors, the shame that left me feeling worthless and isolated—even during those bleak times there was a part of me that thought that it would be ok. I believed that I could get things back on track. I never really knew what that confidence was. I now think part of it was the result of the optimism that comes with privilege. The things that privilege often guarantees—the availability of a basic level of safety and stability regardless of an individual's behavior—tend to foster a degree of confidence about the world at large and optimism about one's ability to navigate it. Even during the times when I was at my worst, I was never homeless. I was never without food. I ate a lot of terrible food, but my basic needs were met. I lost just about every job I got but I was able to get new jobs. It's strange. It's easy to think that this comes from my character or work ethic, but perhaps a lot of it comes from the privilege that I was born into.

"My professor this term said that those with privilege can reach others with privilege much more easily than those without it can. I think that's a responsibility I want to take on moving forward; to continue to educate myself about this and to discuss it with others who may also benefit from privilege without recognizing it."

"Privilege, or lack thereof, is such an important aspect of how systems shape people," Primary Counselor agrees. "Recognizing this provides a deeper ability to understand people and is critical to building trust, and therefore working effectively, with Native Americans, among many others. Is your awareness of this currently affecting the work you're doing?"

"So much, and I'm just getting started. I've been learning about this from the Native American elders at the agency who work as counselors and spiritual advisors. They tell me the difficulties they've had trying to transition from reservations to the large city of Portland. That's one of the reasons that the agency utilizes so much ceremony and spiritual practice like the drumming, talk circles, sweat lodges, and smudging. Ceremony is crucial in Native American culture. Smudging, for instance, prepares a space to be used for healing. I love the sacred elements of Native American practices used in counseling. Sadly, I won't be around it much longer as I'll be starting a new job soon. It's bittersweet, because this is the place I started and I will miss the community and ceremonies. But I found a place that's going to pay much better and I need some financial relief."

"Where are you going?"

"I'm going to prison!" Frank replies cheerily. "I applied and interviewed for a job in July and didn't get it but was called back a few weeks ago and interviewed again. It's a program that works on cognitive restructuring with the goal of lowering the recidivism rates of adult men leaving prison. I don't know much else. I know it's going to be a very different experience from anything I've done so far but it's an awesome opportunity for me and my family.

"When I went to the interview, I got to sit in the counseling circle and introduce myself to all the men. They have this big dayroom and all sixty men sit in a circle. I was a little nervous, felt like I was getting sized up, but also kind of knew that these are my kind of my people. I get crime and bad choices. I know the thrill you get from trying to get away with things. I know what it's like to be a man who doesn't think he needs help from others or is unwilling to ask. I also know that bullshit male stereotype that keeps men stuck and shallow. I think that I can relate well to these men. I hope my recovery will demonstrates that one can change one's life. I'm excited to get in there and start working."

"Wow" Primary Counselor exclaims, "big changes— new school, new job. You seem happy about it so congrats. It's very common in our work for people to change jobs every few years. Some people move for more opportunity or more money, some just want to work with different populations, some get burned out or don't care for the place they work. Making choices that are best for you and your family is important if you want a long career in this field. You will always be leaving people who could use your help, but you will always be going somewhere that needs your help. Don't feel guilty about taking care of yourself."

"Thanks," Frank responds, explaining, "I really have no choice. I've been so stressed out about my income, I had to do it. I also had to come clean to Deena about my money. I told you about the financial cost of the court case. Well, up until last month I was still paying it off. I pay the rent to the landlord for the house we live in, then Deena pays me half the rent.

"In February, I was so broke, I paid half of the rent, just her part, justifying it by how I didn't have money and that I would take care of it as soon as I could. I was also thinking that in March the court case would be finished, not knowing about the second trial, so I hadn't been planning on more lawyer or court fees Well, I did the same thing in March, and pretty much, other than a couple hundred dollars here and there, repeated that until last month when I had to pay back that missed rent. It was around $3,000. I'd never told Deena about it, so I had been lying by omission for months. It sucks and it's not who I want to be in my recovery, but I was just scared and ashamed. I had to tell my landlord, who is not just a landlord. She's been this amazingly supportive person in both James' and my life since 2009. I hated telling her, and she was disappointed and upset, as she should be, and Deena was more upset about the dishonestly than the money. But she was understanding and explained that if this is going to be a healthy relationship, there can be no place for dishonesty. Also, she really challenged my recovery, as she practices rigorous honesty as it states in the Big Book of AA.

"I don't follow the philosophy of AA, something that can cause conflict with us because she doesn't understand my recovery process. And if I'm lying to her, she has more doubt and concern; like maybe my recovery isn't something she can rely on. So this has been a big deal, although not as big of a deal as I had built it up to be in my mind. I saw it as a deal-breaker and all this other catastrophic bullshit. I've been practicing dishonest behaviors for months. That's relapse behavior regardless of the justification. The lying was like a snowball going down a hill; it built momentum."

"Lying has a way of building on itself, which creates tension and anxiety," explains Primary Counselor, "you create your own suffering. How are you repairing these relationships?" Frank considers the question and responds, "I've used my mulligan, so I have to be honest going forward. I actually think it will be easier in the future because through this incident I felt loved. Even more importantly, I felt I was not harshly judged, which is critical with my shame issues. I know Deena was upset but she didn't attack my character. I just need to communicate with her when I'm stressed out. She feels it when something's going on with me anyway. I can at least give her the honest reason that I'm stressed and disconnected.

"My landlord's a different story. She's lived in Denver most of the time we've been renting. She moved back recently and has been living in the house's furnished basement. She told us she wants to have her house back. I think she wanted to tell us anyway and this just made it easier for her to do so. She's so great, though; she said we could have until the end of the school year as she knows how hard it is to find rental places in Portland and she doesn't want the kids' school year to be disrupted. That's so helpful and shows what a wonderful person she is."

"It's nice to hear about landlord compassion. In this town and with this job I hear a lot of the opposite," Primary Counselor comments, "lots of rent increases and people selling units so tenants have to move immediately—what a gift to have time to find a place. Do you have any ideas?"

"Well, we were thinking about renting another place, but the places we could afford are way far out of the city. In town, we'd be paying around $2,400 a month— or more—for what we need, and we can't come close to affording that. So we started throwing around the idea of trying to buy a house. Since I'm a veteran, we may be able to get a VA loan. We have a friend who's a realtor and she introduced us to a lender, so we met with her and she gave us some guidance on what needs to be done first to apply for a VA loan. We have to pay off some debts, but since Deena's been waiting tables at a fine dining establishment and making good money, she's paid off much of what we had to. Thankfully, she'd already been working on hers and we didn't have much. We're trying to get all the documentation to see if buying is possible. Even now, sitting here thinking about being a homeowner makes me laugh. It's seriously something I never thought could happen. I don't want to jinx it by celebrating too much, but going from too broke to pay rent to becoming a homeowner with a new job— shit, no way. The year 2016 may be the one when we see the work we've put in start to yield long-term, life-changing results. It's funny—for years I avoided all things connected with the veteran identity. I was not proud of who I was when I left the military and how I disconnected from the really good friends who served with me. I just focused on alcohol and drugs and not the bonds I'd built through my three-year enlistment. And now, my family may have our own home because of the time I spent in the Army. We can start to build a future with this investment. It really would be a symbol of what Deena and I are capable of doing together. I can't even completely wrap my mind around it yet."

1/12/2016
Individual Counseling Session: 60 minutes

Frank shows up for his appointment on time. He shares that his clean date from all substances is unchanged.

"After a very eventful 2015, how has 2016 been treating you?" Primary Counselor queries.

Frank giggles and states, "Well, I got married!"

"Unbelievable," Primary Counselor replies, clearly surprised, "congratulations!"

Frank responds, laughing, "Thanks, it was a bit of a shocker for many people."

"I'm surprised—I haven't heard you discuss this before. What prompted this joyous event?"

"For us to get a VA housing loan based on our combined income, we needed to be married," Frank explains. "I got to thinking about it and it just made sense, so I started to talk to Deena about it.

"So I ask her to sit down, and I begin with, 'you know, this could be a smart financial move for both of...' and as I'm starting to say this, I notice a look of caution come over her face and her arms begin to cross like the iron gates of a fortress that I will be unable to breach. I stop and say, 'Let me start over; what I mean to say is, I love you and want to spend the rest of my life with you. I want us to have a family home so we can have security and safety and do all the things we want to do.' The gates opened back up and she let me in.

"I bought a ring and asked Alex and James if they were okay with it. I told Alex, 'It's probably hard for you to see this right now, but when you're an adult your judgement of me will come from one thing: how I take care of your mom. Right now, you want to live in a happy environment and have fun and you will think highly of me as a result of our stable home and the adventures we all have together. And these things are important, and I plan to provide them, but when you're an adult you will remember me telling you that I will take care of your mom and then doing just that.' Both boys were okay with it. They just want to be brothers; having a sidekick makes all the difference to them. I called and asked her dad. He said yes, and then talked about Jesus for a while—he loves that guy. And then during an argument with Deena, loosely centered around when I would be proposing, I proposed.

"We got married at the courthouse on December 29th with some close friends around us. I'd never thought about vows before and we both talked afterward about how important they felt, how profound the phrase 'for better or for worse' is. Partly, it's because when you have shame, you always believe you are worse, and you wonder, how could this person be with me when I'm worse? Also, of course our life together will go through good times and bad. We've been there; I will be there. I will think I'm there when I'm not. The important thing is that it is okay being on the worse side of the better-worse spectrum. Life will inevitably present challenges, and they might feel insurmountable, but the "worse" doesn't last forever, especially if we're living according to our values. So just accepting that worse is a present situation and will change will help us get through the hard times, and appreciate when things are better. Contrast makes life so worth it."

Primary Counselor replies, "Well, it sounds as though you both have really clear visions of what you want. Are the steps you're taking helping you meet your goals?"

"I think so. We're pretty close to having all of our information turned in to our loan broker. It's been one thing after another; so tedious. Plus, our bank accounts aren't combined, so we each have to find all our own stuff. We've both had moments where we wanted to give up, and others when we took our frustrations out on each other. At the same time, we've each been there to help the other accomplish whatever's required to get to the next step.

"Obviously, money is central to our getting the loan. This is a very personal area and the process we're going through means that both of us have had the blankets tossed off our financial details. It's felt really vulnerable and naked. I don't think we were prepared for that closeness and exposure. We've already had to deal with much tougher things, though, and this exposure, if we can manage the feelings that come with it, can bring us our house, so we're working very hard together. Each email or text indicating a new crisis, a new fight-or-flight adrenaline surge, gives us an opportunity to support each other. It's been crazy hard. I'd like to think the hardest part is done now, but nothing about this counterintuitive process suggests that that's true."

Primary Counselor comments, "I was just sitting here thinking how much, during the time you and I have been meeting for therapy, we have talked about money. It's been an important factor in your early recovery."

"What's that thing people in recovery say," wonders Frank aloud, "the two quickest ways to relapse are romance and finance? Many of us just break ourselves financially in our addiction, and it's super stressful to have to put out your financial dumpster fire.

"You know, I just started working in the prison at the start of December and our program is designed to take guys who have a high likelihood of recidivism and try to decrease the odds of it. Folks coming out of prison have this financial mountain in front of them made up of things like restitution, court and probation fees, child support, and treatment costs. And what kind of work do they get? If they've got some skills, they can swing a hammer or work in a trade, but if they don't have those skills they will be at Carl's Jr. or in a factory—if they're lucky.

"I think beginning to work in the prison has sparked my own gratitude around money. I had to grind, I had to do what I needed to do to get through these early years of recovery. I can relate to what the men I work with have ahead of them as soon as they walk out of the prison gates. I also know that it can be done: Debt can be paid.

"If your check gets garnished, I recommend looking at that from a positive perspective: You were never going to give the creditor the garnished amount so it's like you have an accountant; one who is also an asshole! You keep finding a way to survive and when that garnished amount gets paid off, you just got a raise, boom! My taxes got garnished for three years but my court fees got paid and I got off probation! And with all that, I got a new job that's paying me well, that I love doing, and that I feel is the kind of work I'm meant for.

"I'm the counselor for a group of 12 guys and we break down situations that come up and work to recognize the feelings and thoughts that arise from each. We talk about how when you have emotions that you struggle to cope with, like anxiety, fear, jealousy, whatever they are—when you're experiencing them, you're thinking is usually not at its peak and you can easily start to think outside of your own values. I get to either interact with my group or with the whole community—sixty guys—and talk about life and where shit went wrong. I may not know as much as other counselors about theoretical approaches and evidenced-based practices yet, but I already have a master's degree in where shit went wrong. I get to bring in everything I'm learning in school. I get to model being in a healthy relationship; being a caring parent, step- and co-parent; and living in recovery. I'm going to buy a house while I'm at this job and can explain that I was once so screwed financially I saw no way out of my financial mess and now I'm a homeowner. I can already tell that these men appreciate hearing the struggles as well as the triumphs; I don't sugarcoat the work that needs to be done. I also like the fact that, for a small period, some of the men I work with can find understanding and laughter and take a break from the realities of incarceration."

4/12/2016
Individual Counseling Session: 60 minutes

Frank shows up for his appointment on time. He shares that his clean date from all substances is unchanged.

"I was looking at my notes prior to this session and I noticed that it's your birthday today, and it's an important one. Happy 40th birthday!" Primary Counselor greets Frank.

"Thanks," Frank responds warmly, "I'm not exactly where I imagined I'd be on my 40th, but there were many times where I didn't think I'd get to 40, so I can't complain. I have my four-year sobriety birthday in two days, which means more right now than turning 40. I don't know if I'd have gotten to forty at all without those four years and I know that even if I did, I wouldn't have what I have now. My mom had me when she was 20 so we share zeros on our birthdays; she'll be 60 this year. Zeros bring reflection and I'm glad my mom doesn't have to reflect on my birthday zero with worry."

"Big week," Primary Counselor comments. "Any special plans?"

Frank thinks momentarily. "Going to have some quality time with family—think we're going to eat somewhere nice this weekend—should be a fun break from house searching. We've been putting in offers for houses like you wouldn't believe. This market is stupid right now. I think we've already put in nine offers. We had a couple accept our offer and we were moving forward and then they stopped it because they decided to fix the roof and try for more money. Here I am, making this change from the person I used to be into a social worker, someone who's supposed to be compassionate and understanding, but there's still something deep inside me that wanted to drive over to those people's house and drag them out of it. Their reneging on our agreement had Deena all broken up; she loved the house. I guess I wanted these folks to have to feel that pain. I wish I had a once-a-year pass that allowed me to get drunk and kick someone's ass. I wouldn't have to use the pass, but if something exceptional happened, I could exchange my pass for a night of freedom from my life's rules.

"Anyway, we're still looking. Our realtor is a badass, she just speeds from one place to the next. I'm trying to keep up with her but she's making moves—she drives us to houses as soon as they come on the market. I like the hustle; she's working hard to get us a house."

"I have friends who are also buying a house right now and what they've told me echoes your experience," Primary Counselor shares. "Do you think the stress is affecting your work or school?"

"I actually think it's the opposite. I think I'm using work and school as distractions—elements of my life that divert me from the uncertainty that comes with searching for a home in this real estate market. At work and school, I have a solid idea of what I need to do and what's coming my way so it's kind of grounding for me. Both are enjoyable.

"I love the job and feel that I have a deeper understanding of it each week. Learning about psychopathology around crime and deviance—seeing how the mind responds to situations and feelings and how certain environments create unhealthy beliefs and narratives—is fascinating. I sit down with these guys at the start of their treatment and we complete an assessment during which I ask them gently about their childhoods. Those who are open or able to share their pasts tell me some traumatic stuff; like unbelievable abuse. Most score exceptionally highly on an Adverse Childhood Experiences questionnaire, lots with big trauma. You just sit in prison and hear these stories and you understand immediately that many of these men are in this place because of what happened to them. I feel as though I'm studying a whole separate field at the same time as social work. I just love the counselor that I'm becoming. The people who share their stories with me are giving me such a valuable gift, such useful experience.

"I found out a few weeks ago that I'll be doing my field placement for my senior year at a substance abuse treatment provider called Medicine Wheel Recovery Services. The two co-directors are friends of mine from when I worked at the Native American treatment agency. They started their own agency but it's a long drive from

Portland. I made a deal with them that I would go to their location if I could concentrate all my work hours into Fridays and Saturdays. That way I can work four, ten-hour shifts at the prison from Monday-Thursday and then work as a substance abuse counselor at their agency on Friday and Saturday. It'll be rough but it can be done. I totally understand why people do college when they're young. It doesn't have to be this hard. On the other hand, at that age you might not know what you want to do or may still be partying too much. At least now I know what the hell I want to do, and I actually believe that I can get it done."

7/12/2016
Individual Counseling Session: 60 minutes

Frank shows up for his appointment on time. He shares that his clean date from all substances is unchanged.

"Well, it seems as though every time we talk there's a lot that's happened in just the three-month interim since our last session," Primary Counselor begins. "I know it's summer now and the school term is over, so how are you doing?"

Frank smiles. "Well, just to be consistent, a lot has happened this time as well. Deena and I are homeowners! Shortly after my last session with you we put an offer in; we actually put in three that day. We got a house not too far from here. We love it. The boys got nice rooms, we have a bathroom in our bedroom and Deena has a huge walk-in closet. Kitchen is big. The back yard is huge. When buying a house through the VA, the house really can't be a fixer upper; it must appraise for the value, so our house is livable and nice. The real project is the back yard. It needs a fence and a deck, and I'm planning to do them myself, so I'm sure I'll learn a lot.

"By the time we bought this house we had put in sixteen offers on 16 different houses—the most our realtor has ever put in and she's been doing the job for 40 years. We had a huge roadblock at the end; seriously thought we were going to lose the house. We had to pay $8,000 at the last minute, which we didn't have.

Thankfully, I had some money saved through a 401K that I was able to cash out, but it was a lightning bolt of stress.

"I couldn't even guess the number of times during this ordeal that one of us wanted to give up, leaving the other one to keep it together. We've been life-coaching each other for the last eight months. Couple that with being in school and starting a new job; I was cool on the outside but inside I've been anxious for months. I understand why real estate agents and the loan brokers make money. They practically became our therapists. I probably need to make amends for some of the things I said to them when I was venting, but they both stayed cool, understood our stress and kept us focused on our next task. These two women did different jobs but both had to emotionally help us through this process. I was in my head worrying, thinking 'my family is going to be homeless' and other dark shit. They got my head back into the game and we have a house because of it. It's hard to wrap my mind around the fact that my decision to go into the Army at seventeen is helping my family buy a house now that I'm forty."

"Your energy and pride over this accomplishment is contagious," Primary Counselor smiles. "You've both put in a considerable amount of work and coped with many stressful moments. One of the great parts of my work is seeing people meet their goals. When you walked into that house, what was it like?"

"A few weeks ago I ran my fourth marathon, and it felt very similar to crossing that finish line. It's the feeling of accomplishment; the result of continuing to grind when you don't want to. And a lot of times I want to be lazy. I could seriously waste an entire day watching *Dateline* or *48 Hours*, happily solving crimes, but that attraction to accomplishing things is powerful once you start doing it, especially if it contrasts with what you've done most of your life. My roles as a husband and dad have ignited a strong desire in me to form and accomplish goals. One goal is financial security for my family and developing home equity is a part of pursuing it. This isn't our house, this is our first house. We will continue to think about how we can us this investment to invest more."

"Life can be attractive when you participate in it," Primary Counselor remarks with a smile, "and you seem to be participating in it fully."

"Things are going well right now. Even James' mom is doing well. She just had a baby girl so James is a big brother, which he loves. Her boyfriend is a pretty good guy. They drink a lot—at least they did prior to her pregnancy. I'm hopeful the new baby will allow them to gather some positive momentum, but that's out of my control. They have the same opportunity to participate in life; it's up to them."

10/18/2016
Individual Counseling Session: 60 minutes

Frank shows up for his appointment on time, sharing that his clean date from all substances is unchanged.

"Now that we're back in the fall, how are you transitioning into the season?" inquires Primary Counselor.

"I'm glad it's fall," Frank replies. "It's my senior year of school and I'm crazy busy, but I feel good about the path I'm on. I have my field placement at Medicine Wheel Recovery Services. It's quite a commute—about two hours, which I drive on both Fridays and Saturdays—but I love working with the two women who are the directors. They work so hard . . . and wear a lot of hats. I've thought about working toward starting my own agency, but after watching the demands on my bosses, I've recognized that there's something calming about not having responsibility for running the show. Each director has a daughter who works there. I love that they're showing their daughters what it takes to be independent women running a business. It's better than anything they'll get from school. You can learn about theory and policy all you want, but what happens when the coffee machine breaks down and you have 9:00 a.m. group? That requires a whole different skillset. You ever been around a room full of people in early recovery who don't have coffee? Shit gets wild."

Frank laughs and continues, "I've only had experience working in Portland—and prison—up to this point. This is in a rural community; lots of meth and heroin in a city that doesn't really have the resources to address it. The police and the courts end up dealing with the addiction health crisis because the community lacks any other intervention method. It feels as though everyone has a probation officer, DHS worker, or no-contact order. Most of the folks at Medicine Wheel Recovery Services who are party to a no-contact order end up in treatment at the agency with the other party to the order. There's so much history among these folks about which the staff has no knowledge. This is something entirely new to me. The effects of drug abuse on generations of families are so visible in these small towns. I'm really glad to be out there helping, but the overwhelming complexity of the problem sometimes makes me doubt that I am."

"I've done work with families in small communities," relates Primary Counselor. "It can definitely feel as though you're just putting a band-aid on a much larger issue, but people respond well to having counselors who care in their communities. It does make a real difference, it's just harder to see it; at least that was the way it was for me. So senior year; a lot on your plate, how are you getting through this?"

Frank considers for a moment before replying. "Really, it comes down to this: I'm going to apply to this thing called an Advanced Standing Master's program at Portland State University. It's basically a way to get your master's degree in one year. So I'd have this year, then one more, with a field placement in both years. It requires 1,000 total internship hours in those two years. I want to have a master's degree, but what I really want is not to be divorced because of it! I must keep my thoughts on the sacrifice my family is making to allow me to be less-than-present, even when I'm with them physically. My mind is always thinking about the next academic task, and often when I'm home, I have a computer on my lap.

"This focus on what needs to be done next is actually the main reason I've had some level of success. I must be mindful of trying to support the family as much as I can, and when I have time with my wife, I must be fully mentally and emotionally present. Quality time is critical. She's not going to play around if during our time together part of me is in my head. It's about the Love Languages®. My wife needs quality time and touch to fill the emotional tank, and that's my job. If it's running on empty, that's on me. She isn't making any unreasonable requests of me, so during those periods, I've got to be there for her. You have to support your supporters in the ways they need supporting, not in the ways you think they need to be supported."

1/17/2017
Individual Counseling Session: 60 minutes

Frank arrives at his appointment on time; his clean date from all substances is unchanged.

"This is our first appointment in 2017, and we started in April of 2012. It's been quite a journey already," Primary Counselor notes. "How's the new year treating you?"

"Wow, can't believe it's been that long already. The year's been good so far, but I have a little stress. Deena and I had our first wedding anniversary and decided to start a tradition of going snowboarding. We drove down to Bend and spent the day on Mt. Bachelor. I had just started snowboarding when I met her. She's ridiculously good at it. Back in the day, she was an instructor at Meadows on Mt. Hood. She's a good teacher. Slowly but surely, I'm getting better, but I fall a lot, and it hurts. Sometimes I fall so hard I don't think I can get up. Snowboarding is one more thing I wish I'd learned when I was young. It's pretty cool, though. I lucked out and got myself a hot snowboarding wife. Sometimes I just stare in awe at how easy she makes it look! Plus, it's something at which she'll always be better than I am."

Primary Counselor reflects, "I remember you saying that you had stopped drinking once for a few months because being drunk was keeping you from experiencing Oregon and its nature. It seems that the life you have now has been a goal of yours for more years than we've known each other. That wasn't the stressor was it?"

"No, not at all" laughs Frank, "that's the antidote! The field placement has been stressful due to these snowstorms; either the roads are too dangerous for me to make the commute, or the agency is closed for the same reason. When I came up with this "foolproof" plan, I didn't even factor in weather. Plus we've never had snow like this during the time I've lived here. If my field placement was in Portland, I could make up some hours reasonably easily, but it's not and I'm falling behind. I still have enough time to make it up, barely, by working through spring break, but some of my classmates tell me how many hours they've done, and I've done only about half of theirs. That kind of freaks me out. I'm sure it'll work out, but it makes me a bit anxious. The combination of work demands, school demands and trying not to freak out at home has turned out to be more of a challenge than I'd anticipated.

"Additionally, my feelings have been hungry, and I've really been eating a lot of sugar. Muffins are getting destroyed. I have muffin dealers all over town and I've been making excuses to hit them up. Since getting sober, the more stress I have, the worse I eat. Of course, this undermines the running. I swear that when I'm out running, I can hear people say, 'Hey! That chubby guy is kind of fast!'

"It was nice to have the winter break off from school to regroup and get ready for winter term. Just two terms left, then I'll have my degree. I applied for the master's program and should know whether I got accepted next month. I think the application process also compounded my stress. But I guess if it takes running and muffins to get me a degree, then so be it."

"What skills do you use to abstain from alcohol and nicotine that you're not using to help with sugary snacks?" asks Primary Counselor.

"I don't have boundaries around it. In fact, I rationalize why I need to eat things that are comforting. I'm not focusing on why I might want to make another choice; sugar doesn't have the same long-term negative consequences as the drug use. I've never woken up in jail because of lemon poppy seed muffins. Deena isn't going to leave me over cookies. When I experience cravings, I have a hard time being mindful enough to recognize those cravings for what they are: A response to a feeling; more times than not, stress. I react and feel like shit afterward. I just like that shot of dopamine that I get from sugar more than I like the feeling of stress, and I'm not putting up much of a fight against it right now."

4/18/2017
Individual Counseling Session: 60 minutes

Frank shows up for his appointment on time and confirms that his clean date from all substances is unchanged.

"It's been consistent over the years that we meet around this time in April—a period that's near your clean date, correct?" Primary Counselor asks rhetorically.

"Yes, got five years a few days ago, which is kind of cool. As you know, the five-year mark is kind of a milestone in the recovery community. Also, I've become really comfortable with the fact that I'm in recovery and that I'm outspoken about it. I have a lot of pride around having dealt with this disease in such a way that my life has been transformed, and I'm not ashamed anymore. Sometimes people who have issues with substances or just don't understand addiction get uncomfortable when recovery is discussed. If people are uncomfortable because I'm in recovery and talk about it with each other, that's not my issue. The exception to this would be if I were trying to convert other people, which I don't do. I try to help people who want the help, but it's up to people to want help—and to want help, they must be able to see a problem. I can only model what recovery can look like and hope that folks are able to see something they want. If I'm in recovery but I'm unhappy and unhealthy, no one's going to be attracted to that. They'll continue to choose addiction, because what would be the point of trading the substance that gives them temporary relief for an ongoing state of unhappiness?"

"That's exactly correct," Primary Counselor agrees. "It's important for people to see that all the work that lies before them in recovery is going to be worth it. It's like you and the stress that came from this lifestyle change. Was it worth it?"

"Without a doubt," Frank confirms enthusiastically. "I was telling the guys in prison the other day that if you continue to stay clean and sober, fix the areas of your life that need fixing, cope with life as it comes and work hard, then the opportunities for positive change in your life will be beyond anything you can imagine at the beginning of recovery.

"I'd never thought about being a counselor, never thought about working in a prison, didn't think I was capable of being half of a happy marriage, didn't even really know what a social worker was, never imagined running a marathon. I just wanted to clean up my life and be a better dad. I couldn't comprehend the possibilities because you can't see it from where you start. You must trust that there is something better than where you are, and you have to work your ass off to get there. I haven't told you, but I did get accepted into the Master of Social Work program at Portland State. If all goes as planned, next June I'll have a master's degree. I would've laughed if you'd told me that would have been possible before my sobriety. It's like saying an overweight guy with COPD could run four marathons with respectable times. That's just as unlikely as the rest of what I accomplished, but I was and I did, and it has me asking myself, 'what you got next for me, recovery? It's like a ladder of goals. I keep climbing; sometimes life makes me go down a few rungs, but I know where I'm headed, and I start climbing again. When I get to a goal, I enjoy it, I let it soak in, but I don't spend a lot of time there. I don't pat myself on the back for too long because I need those hands to keep working, to keep climbing!"

"I understand your process," Primary Counselor acknowledges, "but I also think it would be a shame if you didn't take some time to recognize your accomplishments. You're in your last term before getting your bachelor's degree. This is a major goal that took years to accomplish; a pat on the back is a healthy way to shower yourself with compassion. It's also a time for others who have helped you to be able to feel the joy that comes from this moment. Relish it, it took 41 years to get here!"

"Yeah, you're right. I don't want to count any chickens before they hatch, but I'm close," agrees Frank with a look of pleasure. "I'm not sure, but I think I'm the first to graduate college on my mom's side of the family; first-generation college graduate.

"In addition, this school term is not really all that challenging, so if my grades remain as they are, I will graduate *summa cum laude*. Graduating has been so far away for so long that it's a hard concept to wrap my mind around—good problem to have, though.

"What I'm really excited about, though, is that a week after graduation we're flying to Michigan and doing a whole state adventure. Oh yeah, and I just got my official driver's license back! I've cleared my driving record and have no limitations. So we get to go on vacation and I get to drive through my home state. We're going to visit all of Deena's family and my family. We're going to travel in both peninsulas and Deena will get to see the Upper Peninsula (U.P.). The guys will get to meet all their new family members. In my hometown there's this annual summer event called the Battle Creek Field of Flight Air Show & Balloon Festival that hosts the yearly World Hot Air Balloon Championship. As a kid, I would hang out there the whole week it was in our city. I get to take my guys there. There's also a half-marathon during that time that some of my friends will be running. I've been training hard; I'm not going home to be slow! I get to take a sort of victory lap like the one the band A Tribe Called Quest wrote about in their song 'Award Tour'; go home and see family and experience how different it is being back in Battle Creek as the sober person I am now. That'll be my own personal Award Tour. I miss my family and I've been so busy with school all these years that I just haven't been able to see them as much as I'd like. I'm excited to have all the kids play together. There's nothing better than cousins in the summer!"

7/18/2017
Individual Counseling Session: 60 minutes

Frank shows up for his appointment on time. He shares that his clean date from all substances is unchanged. Primary Counselor starts the conversation with a smile, asking, "Am I talking to a college graduate?"

Frank chuckles. "You're talking to a tired college graduate. It's been a little bit of a whirlwind. I walked across the stage in June, and since the Bachelor of Social Work class was a cohort, I got to graduate with a bunch of friends. At the beginning of this program, I just saw people as competition. Now I care a lot for so many of them. I learned so much about people from the stories they shared in class. It was a profound experience to hear others' experiences, especially those of the people who don't share my privilege."

"Why did you consider them competition?"

"Several reasons. My insecurity, shame, and social anxiety were the big ones. I still have some imposter syndrome. In every new situation, I feel as though I could be exposed as the drunk that I am. I know it's a part of recovery, adjusting to being with the normal people. I have this inner sense that I've duped people to get where I am. But I know rationally that the way I've duped them is by working really hard, learning all I can about my field, reading everything, and internalizing my life experiences into lessons. A person who has insecurity or shame can take their capabilities and earned accomplishments and make themselves think that they're not real and that they could vanish. Plus, insecurity about one's interpersonal skills tends to lead away from, not toward, elective social interaction. Most of my friendships were based around alcohol so even with five years' clean, I still feel somewhat uneasy about my ability to communicate with people. Even though in general I feel my social skills are strong, there's a part of me that still cowers some when I have to just talk to people. My describing most of my relationships as having been based around alcohol can be misleading. For my friends, it involved alcohol, but it was about the friendships. For me, I loved those people, but my main focus was on drinking. But anyway, I realized fast that I could learn everything that was taught to me but if I didn't form relationships with these extraordinary people, I would lose out on what was probably the most important part of my college experience."

Primary Counselor reflects, "You show deep awareness around your process. You clearly value continued introspective growth. And think how much more graduation meant to you because you built relationships instead of concentrating on winning the competition! How was graduation for your family?"

"A lot of fun. It was a celebration for my whole team; we did it! Plus, it was on Father's Day. It was great getting to demonstrate for my sons what I will expect of them as they grow up. I don't necessarily expect them to get college degrees, but I do believe that they should work for what they want. I want them to build a sense of agency to overcome internal and external challenges. I don't want them to settle for a comfortable life that doesn't align with their purpose, and I want them to learn the skills they'll need to build one that does. The journey through discomfort is as important as achieving the desired outcome.

"The school made the graduation ceremony streamable, so my family in Michigan was able to watch. Great that technology allowed them to experience it. I mean, it's one of those things I hope never to forget. I know what it took to earn the right to walk across that stage, and the fact that I did it all still seems surreal to me."

"Were you able to go on the vacation you'd planned?"

"Yeah, we just got back like a week ago. We put 2,200 miles on a rental car and drove all over Michigan! Such a great trip. We all did well. You know, this was the biggest trip we've taken as a family. Among other things, it was the most time we've spent together in a car; in addition, it included each of us meeting a lot of new people. Both of those things can be stressful. There was a chance that we would be too much for one another. But we made a solid team. We were compassionate toward each other when we knew that one of us could use a break from the many new types of stimuli we encountered and we each mostly kept our cool. There was a moment at a putt-putt course where my kids were cheating to beat one another and were fighting, and I got really upset and started to yell but ended up walking away before it really got bad. I wish I could keep myself from reacting like that. Seeing the boys cheat on and lie to each other spikes my anger meter. At work I can try to help people who struggle with these behaviors and I usually stay calm in emotional situations with other people, but my own family is another story. It's hard for me during certain situations to cope with my anger in the way that I want to. I want to react in a way that shows them there are better ways to manage anger. But besides me losing it that one time, we were great."

"You said this was your first-time meeting most of her family. How was that?"

"You know, it had been so long since I saw my family that I was excited to see them and I kind of never took into consideration that James and I were meeting new family. I loved it. Deena's family are very Michigan people. They're very welcoming, genuine, enjoy-the-little-things kind of folks. They threw us a pool party and everyone came out. I got to shake a lot of hands, meet lots of good people. I think it was kind of reassuring for Deena's family members to see that she's found someone she loves and someone to help raise her son.

"Got to meet her dad and her other brother. They were both very welcoming. Her brother gave me some shit, which in Michigan is used to see how well you're going to fit in—basically it's a test to see if you can handle the family. My family does the same, so I knew what was going on and gave shit back. I feel that you don't really know people until you're in their homes and see their pictures; those things tell so much about the family story.

"I'm not sure if I've told you this before: You know my brother-in-law lives with us in Portland? He's great. We couldn't ask for a better guy to be around the kids, and he has a really close relationship with Deena. Well, when he was young, he was in a car accident in which their other brother, Joe, ended up dying. I know the story as I've heard them talk about it, and their mom talked about it when she visited Portland. Well, in Michigan, as we were visiting the various relatives, it really struck me that every home I went to had pictures of Joe everywhere. He hasn't gone anywhere, he's still part of their lives. I couldn't feel the depth of this family's loss of Joe until I stood in the homes of the parents and heard the stories of him as a child and a young man. They still speak about him as though he's in the room—to the point that you just kind of know he is. Seeing all of this somehow gave me a deeper sense of responsibility to this family, like I'm here to help and support Joe's siblings on their long healing process. I don't know, could be the universe trying to connect a bunch of people who can all help each other heal; wouldn't be the first time during this process."

Primary Counselor comments, "You connected with them and now have a deeper understanding of them. What a gift! Many families experience lots of disconnection among members and don't recognize that this disconnection may be a cause of unhappiness. For you to see the impact that grief and loss have had and continue to have on this family—to understand their experience without judgement but with rich empathy because you hear their sorrow—seems important."

"It was powerful," Frank affirms, "I hope it stays with me. I'm not the only one who gained some insight. When we left Deena's family we drove to Battle Creek, where I grew up, to visit my brothers and their families. We did the Hot Air Balloon Championships, Fourth of July, and I ran a half-marathon, which I finished in tenth place! And each of my brothers has two kids so all the kids played a lot.

"There was also a pool party that a friend hosted. Several of my friends from as far back as junior high showed up, plus all their kids. In the past it would've been an event where I'd have had too much to drink and made a scene, but instead I got to introduce my wife and family to all these folks and enjoy how hospitable they were. It struck me how much better that experience was than those times I used social gatherings as an excuse to get drunk."

"It sounds like an ideal summer vacation. Were you able to see your parents?"

"Yeah, that's where we went after Battle Creek. We drove 500 miles north to the U.P., a route that includes the Mackinaw Bridge. While my immediate family lived in Battle Creek when I was growing up, most of my extended family lived in the U.P., so I would make this drive all the time as a kid with my parents. It felt meaningful to drive my sons over that bridge for the first time.

"We went up to L'Anse, Michigan, which is right on the Keweenaw Peninsula and Lake Superior. My grandparents' old house is there. A few years ago my folks bought it and they let us stay there during our visit. It was so nice for us to have our own place after bunking at my brothers'. We like our routines and it was comforting to be able to go back home and just chill, the four of us.

"It's one thing to show people Battle Creek, but the U.P. is a whole different world. My parents and my real father all live up there. Deena was saying she could see herself wanting to live there one day. I told her we should come back in January and see if she feels the same," Frank laughs. "We happen to have been there on one of the eight days per year there was no snow! From there we drove back downstate and flew home. It was a really incredible family-bonding trip, and it was so perfect to come back to our home afterward with our dog waiting for us."

"I can see why you would be tired. That was a lot of new people for everyone, plus lots of other sensory input," Primary Counselor reflects. "There's probably a collective energetic unpacking that your family needs to do."

"For sure," Frank confirms. "We were chilling out and resting the first few days we were home, but then it was time to go back to work. I have a small window before my master's program begins which I'm spending building a deck on the back part of the house, so I've been really busy. Thank god for YouTube, wouldn't be able to do this without it."

"It doesn't sound like a lot of time for rest," Primary Counselor comments. "Are you able to tell when you need to rest?"

"Yes, but it's taken a while to learn that. I've had this thing happen throughout the time I've been in school: Around the seventh week of the term, like clockwork, I'll get tired. I'll start having lots of thoughts about taking a day off or I'll just check out—be there physically but on autopilot mentally. And for the longest time, I thought it was depression or shame trying to get me to give up, so I would focus extremely hard on doing the opposite. Like I'd really dig into what I was doing, or if I actually did take a day off, I'd feel guilty about it. After a couple of years, and feedback from Deena—who is a very attuned partner—I came to see I was just tired. My body was trying to tell me to rest.

"This knowledge has really helped reduce my guilt— just understanding what's behind my desire for a break has allowed me to be compassionate toward myself. I have a ton going on and it's natural for the body to need to recuperate. Now I try to plan ahead to ensure I'm caught up on my responsibilities around that time and then schedule some rest days. It's so easy to let my mind tell me that my normal reactions are a personal deficiency instead of recognizing and accepting that human beings have limitations. Even as I say this, I'm working, building a deck, and about to begin graduate school. I've been in my head trying to figure out how to train for a marathon this year just so I can keep my annual marathon running streak going. Deena strongly suggested that I not try to do everything. Graduate school is already going to have this huge impact on my family. Do I need to take the limited free time I'll have available and use it to train at the level required for a marathon? I think there's some ego involved in that impulse so having Deena as my partner helps keeps me humble and also helps me slow the fuck down."

"It's so important to listen to the body," comments Primary Counselor supportively. "It's a very mindful practice. I think including some mindfulness practice into your recovery would allow you to connect your mind and body more effectively and could have tremendous benefits in all the main areas: mind, body, spirit, family, and community. And it seems as though understanding when to rest will be important as graduate school and full-time work begins."

Frank pauses momentarily. "I think you may be onto something with the mindfulness practice. I can use all the help I can get.

"I don't think I'm going to be working full-time. I'll be working in the addiction medicine department of a hospital doing some addiction and mental health individual and group counseling for my field placement. I'll be there two eight-hour days per week. It's exactly what I requested, and my hope is that it will lead to a job post-graduation. From what I researched, this agency provides really effective treatment for clients and pays staff one of the highest wages in the area. Remember," Frank says, chuckling, "my wife bought the stock, my goal is to get the job that will help it rise!

"And on that note, I had put in my notice at the prison before I went on vacation to allow me to focus on school, but when I told my prison job I wouldn't be able to do both my field placement job and my prison job, they didn't want me to go. The contracted agency I work for in the prison and the treatment funders we work with created a new role for me; a part-time Clinical Supervisor position that includes a small caseload of clients.

"This way I can do both jobs. I'll get a raise at the prison due to my new position and will be supervising the other counselors. I need to pass the test for the second level of Alcohol and Drug Counselor Certification (CADC II) to qualify me to supervise, so I'm taking the test early next month. My MSW program starts next week and I'm signed up for an elective that provides instruction for clinical supervision.

"I've had a lot of support from the people I've worked side-by-side with who say that I would be great at the job. This, of course, helps reduce my self-doubt. It's sort of unreal. I mean, I experienced some success in jobs I held prior to getting sober, but that was due to my ability to—briefly—delude employers. I couldn't maintain the illusion that I was a productive addition to anyone's team for very long. My negative behaviors would soon begin to emerge, growing consistently more extreme until whichever boss it was had to let me go. In light of this, the fact that I now have people from the State of Oregon and the Department of Corrections advocating for me to be a supervisor of other skilled counselors feels kind of nuts. This job offer makes me think about that Portland State professor years ago who told me that, as a person with a lot of privilege, I'd get opportunities not available to people who are oppressed. I'm aware that I have to think about how I use these opportunities to benefit not only my family and myself, but also those who don't have the same advantages. I think I'm up for the challenge; at least I'm going to try. It's exciting because all of my experience supervising at the prison and working at the hospital's addiction medicine department will be so educational. I'll get to see how work stress and vicarious trauma affect our staff's ability to be present with our clients. And how my work/life balance shapes my ability to support my staff. I'm curious to see how all these factors influence one other."

10/24/2017
Individual Counseling Session: 60 minutes

Frank shows up for his appointment on time. He shares that his clean date from all substances is unchanged.

Primary Counselor welcomes Frank, saying "I've been noticing a feeling of joy when I see you on my schedule and I wanted to share that with you. I think it's because of how deeply you share about the life you've created. Sometimes I have to sit with clients who don't want to open up or talk about their lives or their feelings in depth, but you've been consistently engaged throughout our time together. This has made my time with you enjoyable, and I want to thank you."

Frank laughs. "Well for your sake, I hope this isn't the session in which I become an introvert and stop sharing about my life! No, I don't even think it's possible for me to refrain from sharing—I've been looking forward to telling you my news: I bought a sport minivan! It's mine—not a car I borrowed, not public transportation. I saved up for the down payment and did a bunch of research to ensure that this vehicle works well for us. There's room for our kids and their friends in the back. We can fold down the back seat and put Chuck in the back, fold down the middle seats and haul a couch or wood or whatever. Got a good deal and it's mine. I'd told Deena we would be a two-vehicle household and here we are."

"That must feel good," Primary Counselor affirms. "I know how much you've ridden your bike and taken TriMet around town and how much Deena has driven all these years. You needed to surmount numerous obstacles for this to happen, and you did. Well done."

"Yeah, it's funny. Not everyone gets it. Most folks my age have gone through several cars and are driving pretty much the vehicle of their choice at this point. It's just part of their lives. This is the first time I've had a vehicle that's insured and has the right tags since 1999—that's almost 20 years. When I drove during the interim it was 'riding dirty.' It's nice to have a rear-view mirror that isn't being used as a police-tracking device. It might be a used sport minivan, but I've got some serious pride around it; I'm driving it like it's a Tesla. Plus, it's in my budget. I could go break the bank and get something shiny that makes me look like I'm someone I'm not, but I'm not about that. I'm going to keep this vehicle maintained and running for years so I don't have to worry about a car payment and I can focus solely on my college loan."

"I've had clients who've bought really expensive vehicles and at first they were elated, but as months passed, the financial stress increased," Primary Counselor relates. "It really affected their overall health. They had to work more hours to pay for this vehicle, and while they did, it just sat in the parking lot. In most cases, it was ego that wanted the vehicle. It takes some discipline to keep that in check. In a roundabout way, you're saying your education—and your peace of mind—is worth more than a shiny car?"

"For sure," Frank smiles, "the shiny vehicle will depreciate, while the value of my education will appreciate. Once I get the M in MSW behind my name, doors to better jobs and a higher income will open. My decision to go back to school at my age required two things: My belief that my degree would ultimately enable me to make a solid salary and my commitment to offset my college loan with money from a side hustle after graduation. I'm working on both of those things. I also need to make big payments on this loan. I want it paid off in seven years. That's my personal challenge.

"I've got a house that's building equity, so we're already investing in our future. The rest of the money will come from making myself marketable and having something to say. I think that having real expertise in a subject and the charisma to attract people who want to learn about it will create profitable opportunities. I'm hoping to continue to learn as much as I can about addiction and see where it leads me. I'm building up my 'having something to say' by interacting with and listening to all these new graduate students in my MSW program. I hadn't anticipated that I would learn so much from their experiences. I don't get to see most of the friends who were accepted with me into the program very much—our schedules are different, so I'm essentially starting a new social circle and professional network. These folks are all smart, so I've just been trying to listen more this year; scoop up all the knowledge I can."

"How are you balancing everything?" Primary Counselor inquires.

"So far, I've been able to keep all the plates spinning. I took and passed the test to get my Certified Alcohol and Drug Counselor II credential, which enabled me to start supervising. It's really helping financially. I'm working around 28 hours a week and can pay the bills. We're not living comfortably but we can get by. Working at the medical office for my field placement two days per week is very cool. I'm lucky to be there. The people I work with have so much experience and are so skilled. Most have post-graduate school training and specializations; I'm kind of envious of their abilities. And that's new because I've had a saying: "I'm only jealous of runners." When I see runners running when I'm not, I'm envious. But sometimes at the medical office, I get a little—I don't know if it's sad or down—because I'm getting such a late start at my career and these folks are already set up. It's one of those things where you find your passion around 40 but wish you'd found it earlier so you could have already obtained or achieved all that comes with it. But I also know that what makes me so passionate about, and good at, what I do is that I can empathize with and relate to people. I would be far less capable of that without all those years I was out there struggling with addiction. I might have found this profession earlier, but I might have sucked at it without the years I spent with a bottle in my hand.

"In addition to my job and the internship, I'm

completing my schoolwork. A blessing of studying social work is that most of my assignments consist of reading, which is something we do a lot of in our house anyway. If my schoolwork were science-based and I had to sit in a lab to get my work done, this wouldn't have worked, but I can lie next to Deena and we can read together and we're still connecting a little. I can read every night in my house and it doesn't create much of a ripple in my family's lives. So it's getting done. I finished ten credits over the summer just taking it day by day, week by week. I'm trying to take care of myself but I admit that the muffins have been calling my name."

"Many people don't get the opportunity to find their passions and instead have no choice but to do what they must to pay their bills and raise their families," Primary Counselor points out. "You're one of the fortunate ones who gets to do the work you want to do. It's important to show your children what it means to find something they love doing and to try to find a way to make a living at it. If they're truly happy doing it, you'll put more intention into your work, which can result in a fulfilling career and advancement opportunities that can support monetary goals."

"I've been thinking about that lately. James had to start a new school this year since we're in a new school district. I'd written a letter requesting that he be allowed to stay in his old school, but my request was turned down, so I wrote another letter to the new school district superintendent specifically discussing the psychological and emotional benefits James would gain if he remained where he was, but all I got back was some bullshit form letter from the superintendent that didn't even address the points I made. So he's going to a new school, but it's turned out that he's actually kind of relieved. The Japanese Immersion program was stressful, and he spent so much time doing homework that my supporting him around homework and checking it afterward was a big chunk of our relationship. In third grade he was doing more homework than his stepbrother in sixth grade! I'm glad he's getting to take a break, so he doesn't burn out. I learned about adultism in school; i.e., how adults enforce their beliefs and perspectives—basically their own ways of doing things—on kids because they understand life from their own experiences. This directing is done with good intentions, but generally isn't recommended by child development professionals.

I don't want to tell my son's story. His story is not my story. His story is for him to tell. I'm a character in his story and I'm trying to look at what kind of character I want to be. I don't know what the world will look like when he's an adult or even an adolescent, but I'm sure he will still need someone he can talk to who will listen to his experiences as unique to him and not look for areas to fix. It's hard, but I'm trying to listen more to what both my guys are passionate about so I can walk beside each one and help him grab whatever he finds meaningful with both hands."

1/16/2018
Individual Counseling Session: 60 minutes

Frank shows up for his appointment on time and shares that his clean date from all substances is unchanged.

"It's nice to see you in this new year," Primary Counselor declares warmly. "I hope the holidays treated you well. I noticed that it was lightly snowing earlier and I'm wondering if the snow reminds you of any particular periods of your life?"

"Well, as you know, I'm from Michigan, so snow was kind of a big part of my first 25 years. I was actually thinking the other day about this stupid-ass thing I did one night in Michigan. I was living in East Lansing because all my friends were going to Michigan State. We would go to this one bar every Tuesday that had cheap specials and was always packed. Anyway, on this night, I was wasted as usual. A friend asked me to go get us both drinks at the bar and gave me money for them. I stumbled up to the bar…and then just changed my mind and walked out without a word. I didn't tell my buddy. I still had the money he had given me. I was hungry and walked over to a little convenience store and stole two boxes of Pizza Rolls. I didn't remember that I still had my friend's money. I started to walk home, which was probably around three-quarters of a mile away, in the freezing cold. The sidewalk was all icy and I was slipping and falling the whole way home. People were driving by honking and yelling. I must've been quite a spectacle. When I finally got home I was bloodied, had scratches and cuts, and my clothes were mangled. My roommates were all wondering what the hell happened to me. I told them what happened and how excited I was to eat the Pizza Rolls I'd carried home. The only thing is that I'd carried a box in each hand and since I fell so much, the boxes—which are supposed to have something like 15 rolls in each box—were totally destroyed. I made it home with literally three Pizza Rolls between the two boxes. That is what winter looked like for me for most of my adult life—just a mess."

"I'm doing my best not to laugh at that story," Primary Counselor confides, "as it does sound as though life was more challenging for you at that time than it had to be. Well, what's the contrast now? Contrast is key, right? If things are not different in recovery then why would you continue to be in recovery?"

"The contrast is significant," Frank answers. "A few weeks ago, Deena and I went up to Mt. Hood to go snowboarding for our anniversary and we had a great time. Being able to afford a day at the mountain plus an Airbnb and go out to a nice dinner—that's a night-and-day contrast to my life before I got sober. Another contrast: In Michigan I had a truck with a slider window. I broke it when I crawled through it after I had locked my keys inside the cab. I couldn't afford to replace the glass—although I had money for booze—so I just put a piece of cardboard up in its place and drove around with the freezing winter wind whipping around me. In comparison, for Deena's and my trip, I got to drive my fully-functional vehicle that I take care of and appreciate. The ride was *so* much more comfortable!

"Another area of growth: Deena and I realized we had both been a little short and irritated with each other in recent months. We talked about it on the way to the mountain and decided that we just hadn't been noticing all the things we do for each other and what we're grateful for in our relationship. We came up with this idea to text each other each day noting one thing about the other person that we're grateful for. We can't reuse any previous observations; it has to be a new thing each time.

"We've been doing it for about three weeks now and it's made a difference. We've both been kinder and more loving toward each other. I think we all feel loved when our positive qualities are noticed and appreciated. I've also noticed that when I actively look for and note Deena's positive qualities, I feel more loving toward her.

"I think it's common for couples to get in a rut and be critical of one another, or at least it has been for me, so this is a great plan of action to try to get out of the rut and to build a more positive and supportive connection. In my past relationships I didn't have those conversations or spend time thinking of ways to reconnect in a loving way with a partner. I would just blame the other person and cling to resentments.

"Just having gratitude in general is new to me, even though I've had things to be grateful for my whole life. The practice of looking for things I'm grateful for was the opposite of what my addiction wanted me to do; gratitude is kryptonite for addiction. I can't be happy and grateful for all I have and still have a compulsion to avoid and numb all my feelings. Those two states are incongruent. I need shitty feelings so I have permission to numb them, so I manufacture shitty feelings by noticing the ways in which my life sucks and judging myself as a piece of shit for making it that way. That's addiction's cookbook."

"How are you doing as far as the recovery goals you have planned this year?" asks Primary Counselor.

"I'm on track. Going to graduate in June. I'm almost sure my parents are going to fly here to watch. Kind of means a lot. While I'm older and doing this for myself and my immediate family, deep down I still want my parents to be proud of me. I think that's a pretty universal desire. Plus, I want them to see the life I've created here.

"The last time they were here James was just over a year old. We all drank a lot. It was fun, but a lot has changed. It may be a little uncomfortable for them since there's no drinking in my house, but they know that and still want to come.

"One goal I have is to get a paid position at the hospital where I'm currently doing my field placement. To increase my chances, I treat each day there like a job interview: I make sure my clothes are ironed and that I'm visibly working hard, demonstrating how dependable and team-oriented I am. I've learned from managing others that having a team member who can just work well with others for 40 hours a week is a big deal. By extension, having someone who's positive and funny can really improve a team's morale and productivity. I try to be that guy.

"My only other real goal is running another marathon later in the year. I've begun to put together a training schedule and am trying to find ways to run more.

"I feel confident all these things are going to happen, which will make for a pretty great year. Deena's happily anticipating my graduation. Currently, school holds my attention and takes a lot of my time and energy. That energy will need someplace to go, and that place will be home. I'm not sure that when Deena's looking forward to having more of my attention she's really considering how she'll feel once I'm actually all up in her space. It's totally one of those 'be careful what you wish for' scenarios."

4/17/2018
Individual Counseling Session: 60 minutes

Frank shows up for his appointment on time. He shares that his clean date from all substances is unchanged.

Primary Counselor begins the session, "I'm not sure if you know this, but this is our second-to-last session. Your part of the study is nearing completion. When we're done today, I'll give you a questionnaire to fill out at your leisure and then we can review it at the next session. How are you feeling about your part of this ending?"

Frank pauses to think. "I was a little uncertain when this would end. I just got my six years clean and I knew the study was six years so I knew we were close. Just seems surreal that we've been sitting in this office having these conversations for six years. And the fact that it's still the two of us is cool. I know the turnover rate for this work is high—shoot, I've already switched jobs, and if things go right, will switch again in a few months. I feel fortunate you're still here. It would have been weird to have finished this with someone else. No one else would know how close I came to quitting during that first year or how close I came to relapsing while James was living away from me. You've been a rock—a steadying force throughout it all. It's something I'm really grateful for. Now that I've done research for school, I'm kind of wondering how my experience might affect the findings of the study. I know not everyone has done well.

We lost Tom while I was in treatment, and I've run into a number of other people from treatment and some are drinking again. I've even had clients in the correctional program who were in DISP. So am I the outlier, or are they?"

"It's so interesting that you began this study without the knowledge that you now have about research studies. Just for some transparency, this is not a study that focused on the quantitative outcomes. The percentage of people who were successful is not what this study was designed to determine. Plus, 'success' is very difficult to define in a way that would be useful in this case. Is success sobriety from alcohol, or ceasing to drink and drive, or some other program-defined goal?

No, this study was designed to determine why DISP participants either met or failed to meet the goals they themselves established. We want to explore what aspects of our clients' lives determine outcomes. The questionnaire provides an opportunity for you to share with us those elements of your life, both the positive and the negative, that had an effect on your meeting your goals. At your next session, we will also read over your clinical documentation from different time periods during the previous six years.

We ultimately hope to learn not just what people find generally helpful on their journey toward their goals, but at what time periods within treatment different experiences might be most beneficial. We want to learn more about what clients need at different stages of their recovery and what patterns of behavior might reflect that a client is struggling. Once we gather and analyze that information, we'll be able to integrate our findings into our recovery model."

"Hmm," Frank pauses momentarily. "I like that you're working to improve the program's success rate. My research teacher would say that social work research needs to help its subjects while they're being studied. I think that the additional three and a half years we've been meeting post-probation have provided me with critical support. Having someone to talk to and to help me hold myself accountable has really helped me. I've had some of my toughest challenges in recovery during these three and a half years, including living without James, the court cases, trying to pay for the court cases, buying a home and ongoing co-parenting stuff. It's created stress in my relationship—now marriage—and it's all occurred after my mandated treatment period. I know that having this continued counseling has helped me find ways to deal with all that. I also hope that what I've shared throughout this experience will help some folks who come after me. Doesn't it seem weird that this is ending at almost the same time that I'm finishing school?"

"The simultaneous ending of these two things feels almost fateful," agrees Primary Counselor. "What is it you like to say? 'The universe had something to do with it?' Perhaps there are larger forces at play here. How are things going as far as school nearing completion?"

"I'm ready to be done. I'm running on fumes. Fortunately, I don't need a lot of credits because I took an extra class last summer. I'm also ahead in my hours at the field placement, so I'll be done with that weeks before graduation. My parents are flying in from Michigan. We're going to have a graduation/house-warming/got married party the weekend of graduation. We really haven't been able to celebrate, so I have lots of stuff to do around the house to get it ready. I'll be busy, which will keep me busy up until the end of graduation.

I'm trying to stay present for this; I tend to get focused on what's next and I definitely have some 'what's next' things looming, but this is a big deal for everyone, and I want to enjoy it. I'm graduating with a couple people with whom I've been in school for about five years. We've all experienced a lot of change and I want to reflect on all that's happened. A social work education fosters a tremendous amount of self-analysis and reflection. Plus, a lot of life happens in five years! My classmates and I are not the same people we were when we started this process.

"For perspective, I have this picture of James that I love from when he was in preschool. It shows him trying to write his name. That picture was taken almost to the day that I started school. He was four. He will be ten years and four months old in June and finishing fourth grade. That's how long we've been doing this. He's always been my biggest cheerleader, from the days of helping me with my Japanese homework through today.

"I get to do this final project for this class that summarizes my educational experience. I'm going to record a podcast and have my sons be the hosts and ask me social work questions. My education's always been a family project—seems only right to have it end that way!"

"I'm sure your kids are happy to be included in it," Primary Counselor replies warmly. "Well, we're nearing the end of the session so I'm going to give you the study completion questionnaire. We hope that you'll take the time to really consider the questions and examine and reflect on your experiences during the last six years as you work your way through it. I can see you have lots going on in the next few months. If you end up having difficulty finding the time to complete it, just communicate that and we'll postpone your exit interview. Please don't rush just to get it done; we would much rather wait to have it completed when you can think about the questions in depth.

"This last interview will be an hour and a half. The first half hour you will be meeting with me for an individual session. Following that, you and I will spend an hour reviewing and discussing your responses to the questionnaire with three members of the committee responsible for the study's design and administration. One is the case manager from DISP, another is the judge who presides over DISP and the last is the director of this treatment agency. Some people get nervous at the thought of discussing their experience with and thoughts about the program with new people; we understand that it can be anxiety producing. I just want to assure you that this will be a positive experience. These people all just want to congratulate you and hear how you did it. How does that all sound?"

"I'm not nervous at all," Frank replies enthusiastically. "I love talking about this stuff. This is literally the proudest of myself I've ever been. I just hope I can share it all in an hour!"

7/17/2018
Exit Interview-Individual Session: 30 minutes

Frank shows up for his Exit Interview on time. He states that his clean date for all substances is unchanged. Primary Counselor reiterates that the appointment will consist of a 30-minute individual session followed by the hour-long Exit Interview.

"This appointment is bittersweet for me," reflects Primary Counselor. "I'm happy for you that you've completed the study and will be continuing on your chosen path. Simultaneously, though, I'm also feeling some sadness about the fact that I won't have the opportunity through these appointments to hear about your progress any longer.

"I'm assuming that things have gone as planned since our last meeting. If so, you've completed your graduate program and received your Master's in Social Work, so congratulations are in order!"

"Thanks!" Frank enthuses, "I'm officially a master of something! At least in title. Not going to lie—it feels so damn good to be done. And I don't think it's really hit me yet, although it's feeling more and more normal not to have so much to do. I think I can get used to it!"

"It's quite an accomplishment!" declares Primary Counselor. "And one that can never be taken from you.

How was the celebration?"

"It was fun. I enjoyed seeing the joy and relief of my fellow graduates as well as that of my family. You know, my wife, stepson, and brother-in-law—three of the four main people in my life—have never known me as a non-student.

"And James was four when I started, so except for some early memories, he doesn't really remember that either. This is a new place for all of us. I really hope to direct some positive energy toward them now that I won't be racing around so frenetically. They've had my back, observing and enduring the process alongside me. They're amazing!"

"You've frequently noted the sacrifices they've made," Primary Counselor comments. "I can tell how supported they've helped you feel. Did your parents come out for the graduation ceremony as planned?"

"Yes," Frank chuckled, "I think Deena has a little better understanding of me after having my parents around for a long weekend. My mom and I share a lot of qualities. Both of my parents stay busy—my house has never been so clean and organized. They get up super early and just clean.

"It was so helpful to have them around for the party. They love that stuff: going around to all the stores to get the various things we needed and doing food and decoration prep. They were on it; kind of ran the show. My buddy smoked a pork shoulder the whole night before the party so we had pulled pork sandwiches and just about everything else you could think of."

"Our parents do provide insight into how we became who we are," Primary Counselor comments. "I know you discussed not having alcohol in your home and that your parents drink. How was that during the weekend?"

Frank considers the question. "It was telling. Let me say this first: The weekend was great and my folks were helpful, enjoyable and supportive. The third night they were here we went to my friend's house—the one who smoked the pork shoulder. This is my best friend; someone I've known since we were in high school and whom my parents have also known since then. He's kind of like another son to them. We went out to his place so they could see his farmhouse and several friends came; it was a party. Everyone was drinking besides Deena and me. I wanted my parents to have a night where they could enjoy themselves and have some beers with friends. Deena and I were fine. We had an almost perfect time, helped by the fact that we knew we could leave at any point we wanted—I've found it's important to my sobriety to make sure I don't feel stuck around people when they're drinking. So there were lots of kids, delicious food, hanging in the country outside of town; ideal for some folks from the Upper Peninsula of Michigan. My parents had a blast. We all did. The next day was the party at our house. We had a lot of errands to do and then needed to set up for the party, so we were pretty busy getting everything done. People started showing up and eating at about noon and the party went on for four hours with people showing up at different times throughout. There were countless introductions and greetings and the general socializing that happens at these sorts of events. After a few hours, I happened to notice that my folks were isolating a little bit; not away from everyone, but really keeping to themselves a bit to the side of the rest of the people. They would say the right thing when introduced and were on top of party responsibilities that arose, but their ability to mingle and connect with people at this party was much different than I had seen it at the previous party. They were pretty much hip-to-hip during the graduation party, and it was clear they were uncomfortable. I talked to Deena about it later.

"I really empathized with them at that moment because I've been there: Not knowing how to socialize with people when I or they weren't drinking. Just sitting there with your insecurities showing so much it feels like you're not wearing pants. In that moment, I could see myself almost childlike, at the period when my development stopped as I started drinking and learned to socialize in that context. All those years of blaming and judging them for their alcohol-related behaviors—I kind of felt silly as I watched these two people in their 60s sitting securely close, dreading the next introduction. All these years I've asked myself 'Why do I get so uncomfortable in social situations without a drink?' Observing and empathizing with the discomfort they exhibited gave me real insight into the origins of my own social anxieties."

"Wow," Primary Counselor exclaims, "I will never stop being surprised by the gifts empathy can bestow. Think of that insight, and the years' worth of work you did so that when that scenario unfolded in the exact manner it did, you were able to interpret your parents' behavior. All those things lined up: the universe provided an opportunity for you to observe them in this alcohol-free social situation and then you really reflected with empathy on what you saw. I know the concept of love is abstract and difficult to define, but that moment feels like love."

"Hmm," Frank considers Primary Counselor's words, then continues "that makes sense, because love requires a certain level of connection. Life gives us so many ways to insert barriers into connections; barriers that can last for decades. I think that in that moment at the party, some of those barriers between my parents and me eroded and I felt more connected to them than I have for as long as I can remember. It's quite possibly the most connected I have ever felt to them. And they didn't even know it happened. Connection doesn't need to be a team game; it requires awareness of the barriers that disconnect us and the use of empathy to get past them."

"I love that," Primary Counselor enthuses, "and I'll think of that often. Sadly, we're running out of time. Anything else happen in the last few months?"

"The only thing I can think of is that I interviewed for a job at the hospital with the addiction medicine department where I completed my field placement and got it. I start next Monday. It starts as an on-call position but that's apparently how you get in, and I was assured I would eventually get full-time hours Monday through Friday, so that's the next step. It's working where I want to work and making a wage that feels livable. When I get hired there full-time, I'll also have amazing health benefits for my whole family. One at a time, I'm reaching the objectives on my goals ladder, and then moving on to the next."

Exit Interview: 60 minutes

The Exit Interview is a 60-minute interview conducted by a four-person panel consisting of the Primary Counselor, the DISP Case Manager, Multnomah County Judge Smith who presides over the legal branch of DISP, and the Treatment Agency Director. Frank is asked by the DIPS case manager if he has completed the Exit Interview Questionnaire, to which he responds that he has. The DISP case manager then informs him that to officially complete the exit interview, she will ask Frank the questions it contains, in answer to which he should read his written responses.

Exit Interview Questionnaire

Did you complete DISP?

"Yes, I completed DISP in November of 2014."

Did you receive the six-month early release from DISP?

"Yes, and I am very grateful for the reduction in probation time."

While in the study, did you relapse? Why do you think this did or did not happen?

"I have not relapsed since I stopped using all substances shortly before starting DISP in April 2012. As of today, I've been clean and sober for roughly six years and three months.

"My son was my primary motivator to get sober in the beginning, as I knew the legal consequences of a relapse would negatively affect him as much as they would me. I felt a lot of shame and guilt about the fact that my alcohol-related and criminal behaviors made my son's life more difficult, and I knew that I wanted to be a better father. This rising awareness of the negative effects of my substance use on those around me motivated me to succeed in treatment and recovery.

"Shortly after entering DISP I started running—for exercise, and to try to literally dissipate some of the energy accompanying the difficult feelings that arose in me as a result of my learning to deal with life's challenges without alcohol. This turned out to be tremendously effective for diminishing the stress, anxiety, and boredom that I was experiencing in early recovery. I began to feel better physically, and I was proud of myself each time I managed to run further and faster than the week prior. This pride contrasted significantly with my complete lack of self-esteem just a few months before starting the program. In early recovery, each time I was triggered and chose to go for a run instead of to have a drink, my brain's recognition that there are ways to cope with challenging emotions that don't involve substance use deepened.

"AA also helped. Even though I'm not a big AA guy, hearing other people's stories helped to normalize what I was feeling and experiencing.

"In addition, about eight months into DISP, I was able to go back to school with the newfound knowledge that I wanted to work with people struggling with addiction. I've had lots of academic success since then but those first few terms were crucial because that's when I learned to juggle life as a single parent, a student, and a runner while still attending DISP as required. I got a taste of how good it feels to set goals and accomplish them. Working toward my career goals gave me a purpose, which was also new for me. It's taken a lot of hard work combined with finally recognizing that I needed to change the joyless way I lived to bring me to this place: Standing here before you today, sober."

Did you receive any Notices of Parole Violation? Why or why not?

"I received two parole violations, both in the first eight months of the program. The first time I lacked the 40 dollars necessary to pay for a required UDS, so I just didn't submit one. I didn't perform any action afterward to indicate that I understood that it was my responsibility to make sure I had the money for it. This resulted in a probation violation for which I received a day in jail.

"My second violation consisted of arriving late for group, which is considered a missed group. In response to this second failure, I proactively chose to perform community service for Meals on Wheels the weekend after I missed the group. I called my Case Manager first thing the following Monday morning to explain what had happened—thereby demonstrating that I was holding myself accountable for my actions—and shared with her the service I had performed in place of group. For that parole violation I stood in front of you, Judge Smith. You stated that you appreciated my choosing to take responsibility rather than to make excuses for the missed group, and you sentenced me to the community hours I had already completed with Meals on Wheels."

During the three phases of the program study (1. treatment, 2. post-treatment on probation, and 3. post-treatment off probation [study participation continuing]), what were the most challenging aspects of each phase?

"The most challenging part is difficult to determine, as there were quite a few hurdles throughout, but the financial demands of this program might have been the most difficult aspect of it for me. I have this saying that 'I try not to judge a shift I didn't work,' meaning that I can't fairly evaluate a situation without the informational context. So I'm aware that I'm not privy to the inner workings of the DISP. I know there are costs to running a program like this one, and I'm sure that participants' financial contributions don't even come close to covering those costs. At the same time, I'm intimately acquainted with the difficulty of finding the money required to participate in the program, as well as with the overwhelming stress the financial requirements added to my life at an already difficult time.

"I paid over $800 in program fees each month for the first three months. I made around 14 dollars an hour at that time, which made it very difficult to pay for the program, pay my bills, and feed my son all in the same month. This in no way minimizes the fact that this program saved me from continuing my cycle of addiction and immeasurably improved my life, and I know I had to have consequences for my incredibly poor decisions. However, I feel it's important to note that extreme financial stress can cause folks to resort to some pretty unhealthy thinking and behaviors.

"In addition, those who can't afford this program, and as a result fail to get sober, perpetuate the narrative that addicts are not willing to work for the change they need. It furthers the stigma that connects addiction to weak character and the inability or unwillingness of addicts to take responsibility for themselves.

"Finally, the financial burden of participating in the program is so high that I know many people who won't even try it because of its costs, which means that numerous people who might benefit from it lack the opportunity to try.

"Assuming that the overall objectives of the program include helping as many people as possible get off of addictive substances and become contributing members of society, financially blocking the most powerless and indigent addicts from participating in it may not optimally serve the program's goals.

"However, to go back to my own experience— separate from the cost issue I just mentioned and my presumption that my difficulties in this area might suggest more general program concerns—I found that things got easier for me in the middle of the program when I was on probation but no longer in weekly treatment. This was true for a few reasons. Life as a student provided a lot of structure for me, as did my son's school schedule, my running, and work. I learned time management skills, which were critical because my weeks were so busy and I had a lot of goals to meet. During this period, I also learned how to be a good student, which often meant allowing extra time for assignments and proof-reading things more than once because I had been out of school for a while. And I learned how to use a computer. I'd had some PC experience previously but I couldn't type and really didn't understand many of the computer programs that I needed to use for school. I had so much to learn that it sometimes felt overwhelming, but it also kept me focused on my goals.

"The last part of the program was also difficult for me due to events in my personal life. As soon as I got off probation, I became involved in a custody battle.

I hadn't known I could experience the degree of hurt that followed or worry that much about my son. Not to mention the stress it caused in my current relationship; I wouldn't wish it on anyone. I thought often during that period that it would be a nice time to have a drink! Even though I can sit here and tell you all the reasons why that wouldn't have helped—and would instead have actively harmed me and everyone I care about—I can still vividly imagine the short-term relief that a drink would have provided. Getting through that situation sober, having to communicate about what was going on with me to people, including my wife, and asking the universe for help made me uncomfortable all over again because I had never done any of that before. And I did it clean and sober! If I'm lucky, that will ultimately prove to have been the hardest period of my life."

What was/were the most important lesson(s) you learned from this experience?

"I've learned so many things, including how important it is to be open to learning. Most of my adult life I was not willing to hear others' ideas, which I realized early in this process had to change if I was going to succeed in the program. I think openness and willingness have been crucial to learning as much as I have. I've learned more in the last six years about every single area of my own life and about the world in general than I'd learned in any decade before.

"Another lesson is the importance of making goals around the things in my life that bring me joy. I think it can be easy to let life and career goals get in the way of other areas of your life. I enjoy running, so making time for it is important to my overall well-being. Running, much like coaching and snowboarding or exercising with my wife, is something outside career and educational goals that brings me joy and escape.

"I've been able to go to graduate school and find a career that will help my family live a financially secure life. I've gone from running a half a mile in jeans in the first few months on an impulse because I was frustrated about co-parenting issues to training for my fifth marathon, which I will complete in a few months.

"I've also learned the importance of helping and giving back to the people who have helped me. I like to call this 'supporting your supporters.' And it doesn't have to be people who did huge things for me—the little stuff is important to acknowledge, too. When I posted a picture of my three-month sobriety coin on social media, many people took the time to privately message me to explain how addiction has personally affected them, and I can't even tell you how much that stuff helped me. Addiction is such a pervasive problem. I could talk for hours about the many ways that so many people have helped me get here, so I'm working to be conscious of their help and to try to give back in any way I can.

"There have been other significant lessons, but these are the most important."

What is your most important accomplishment?

"I'm going to mention several important accomplishments, but first I would like to acknowledge that none of them would have been possible without the six-plus years of sobriety I have currently, as well as the almost five years without cigarettes. I've already touched on a lot of my big accomplishments, including getting married and working on being a healthy part of a healthy relationship; going through the court process to ensure that my relationship with my son is legally secure; buying a house; earning a master's degree; getting a job after graduate school; and running four, almost five, marathons. Oh, yeah, and completing DISP. The only objective in my mind at the start of this was to complete my probation and stay sober. All the rest are things I could never have imagined; I still find the fact that I did them all pretty mind blowing."

What is your biggest regret or disappointment?

"I don't think I have too many regrets; everything has served its purpose and the struggles have been as important as the triumphs. However, if I had to pick something, I'd say it's missing the opportunity to qualify for the Boston Marathon. Early in my senior year of college I ran a three hour and 24-minute marathon time, which was nine minutes off the qualifying time of three hours and 15 minutes. Senior year of undergrad, followed by graduate school and working two internships, meant

I just didn't have the time to run as much as I would have liked. One of my life's goals is to qualify for Boston and I'm worried that I may have lost that opportunity. It might not seem like a big deal, but I've envisioned myself qualifying so many times that I felt pretty confident that it was a goal I would attain. I haven't completely given up hope, but the possibility feels further and further away now."

How have you learned to cope with cravings or urges?

"This has changed as my experience and education around coping strategies have grown. In the beginning, I would run a lot when I was craving. I would also just watch tv which sounds strange to say but that first year Netflix was a huge support. I just knew that if I left the house my risk of relapse would increase. A lot of the time I would have my son, so after he went to sleep or on nights he was gone, I'd watch *Breaking Bad* or some other series. I had to stop watching *Mad Men* because every scene was drinking, smoking, or womanizing, and that was all I wanted to do. But the distraction of the other shows definitely helped. As I began reaching some of my initial goals and went back to school, I really started to like myself again and simultaneously found I enjoyed learning. I did have thoughts of wanting a drink but I had no illusions about what would happen if I had one. I knew I would lose everything I had gained, so I didn't allow my imagination to minimize the impact a lapse would have on my life. And the things I would be essentially trading for a drink are things I enjoy much more than alcohol. My thoughts transitioned from "Why can't I?" to "Why would I want to?" which was a big change in perspective and awareness."

Any changes in physical and/or mental health during the study period?

"I think this can only be answered by stating that the changes have been substantial. Healthwise, I was a mess when I started. I mean, being alcohol- and smoke-free for this time period has significantly improved my quality of life. I sleep better, I eat better and I haven't had a hangover for over six years, which would make the whole ordeal of getting sober worth it by itself. One thing I didn't see coming, and I want to say this in the most inoffensive manner possible, but pooping is an overall more enjoyable experience. No one talks about how screwed up your GI tract gets from alcohol! I also had a doctor tell me I had COPD prior to entering this program, and I've now run over 5,000 miles since I got sober—it really feels like a total transformation.

"As far as my mental health goes, I'm just more aware of the symptoms of depression, shame, anxiety and stress I experience and how they all intertwine. My shame has really been neutralized by the pride and purpose I've gained from living a life that aligns with my values.

"I've had a strange relationship with anxiety over the years. I've historically had racing thoughts about the things that I need to do. This manifestation of anxiety actually helped me stay on top of the many things I've had going on while in the program. I rarely forgot tasks because I thought about everything so much. Running provided a great opportunity to take all that information and sort it out, prioritize it, and come up with a plan to tackle it. I would use it to prepare my approach to school material. I would start by reading over an assignment, then I'd go for a long run. By the time I was done with that run I would have a good idea of what I wanted to do and how I wanted to do it. I'm actually a bit concerned about what I'll do with all of that mental energy now that school has stopped, because my newly-freed focus will require a subject. I just need to guide it toward areas that could use the attention and not toward areas in my life that are outside of my control."

What has been the biggest surprise of this experience?

"Before starting this program, I could never even have imagined this life, so this has all been a wonderful surprise. However, if I had to pinpoint one thing, it's my becoming a counselor. For most of my life I've been in my own head; my swirling thoughts focused on me and in some way or another on alcohol. The five years prior to getting sober I had a hard time listening to people, even my closest friends. I would look at them when they were talking and nod my head as though I was paying attention, but I struggled to participate and engage in conversations. Engaging in meaningful conversations is now what I do for a living. I watch for clients' physical responses to questions. I try to listen with empathy to better understand their experiences and any unmet emotional needs that might be contributing to their struggles with substance use. And most importantly, I remain attentive to clients' implicit and explicit clues and try to read between the lines of their narratives to gain as much insight as possible into their experiences. Now that I put less energy into worrying about my own insecurities, I'm more effective at caring for others. The contrast between my life now and how I lived when I started this program continues to amaze me."

What are the potential risks to your recovery?

"I feel that I've surrounded myself with people who will definitely let me know if they sense something's amiss with me. Having a wife and a brother-in-law in recovery feels supportive as they know what the deal is and what my regression would look like. I also believe that working in the recovery field keeps me connected to the rawness and pain of addiction. I don't have a lot of room in my life to entertain thoughts of 'Wouldn't it be nice if I could have a drink?' or 'Alcohol would make this better,' because I see people daily who show me what that thinking leads to. Health problems, injuries for which I would need painkillers and/or marriage conflict are all areas anyone in recovery should be mindful of, and I'm no exception. My getting into a cycle of negative thinking would be a warning sign that bigger issues may be looming, such as depression, shame, or resentment, all of which I would need to talk to someone about. I feel that I've formed great relationships during my years of sobriety and can reach out to people when I need to."

What have been your biggest "Aha" moments?

"I've had so many experiences that have shown me my path. I've followed that path and it's improved my life and the lives around me. I had a moment in an AA meeting which opened me to spirituality and life's lessons. In a separate incident, I was unemployed and went to a veterans' job fair and a woman handed me a piece of paper explaining a program that would allow me to go back to school. This happened at a time when I wanted to go back to school, which is different from thinking: 'I should go back to school because that's what successful people do.' That moment, reading that piece of paper and knowing I had a chance to earn a degree and become a counselor, and trusting that it was what I had to do—I still get goosebumps thinking about it. I've had at least five similar experiences in sobriety in which I've encountered a meeting of my needs with a seemingly random but complementary opportunity. It makes me wonder how many occurred all those years before I got sober that I was too drunk to notice."

The panel pauses the questioning and Judge Smith remarks:

"We have just one more question for you. However, before we ask the question, we want to share how appreciative we are of the level of detail you've provided about your experience in, and thoughts about, our program. We will certainly take into consideration what you've shared. Your story is interesting in that you started this process as a participant, and you are finishing this program as our colleague. We are all proud of all that you accomplished while in this program. Your transformation is quite remarkable, and you deserve every ounce of the pride that you feel. Every person on this panel has had some interaction with you during this period, and all of us have seen you interact with your son. It has been a pleasure, Frank; you are a great example and reminder of why we do this work. I speak for every one of us when I say congratulations on the work that you have done while in this program."

What are your plans for the future?

"Before I answer, I also would like to thank you, Judge Smith, and everyone on the panel. I cannot adequately express how much I appreciate all the time and energy you each put into helping me through the last six years. As for my future: In recovery we call this future-tripping, something which is typically frowned upon. However, I do have a lot of goals that I'm either beginning to work toward or have in mind as plans for the future.

"I want to travel with my family, because they deserve it, and I want to have those memories while our kids are still young. I want to buy another house or two for rental properties to invest in my family's future and my two sons' educations. We've considered moving back to Michigan to be closer to family or maybe somewhere outside the city with a little piece of land. And I would love to create a running trail on that piece of land and run it for the rest of my life.

"More broadly, I intend to start doing some community social work. I want to use exercise and community to help people who are struggling with addiction. I know the benefits I've gotten from running and I'd like to share them with others who might be interested. Something like a weekly running group of people in recovery sounds like a blast. I love that about social work: That it can expand into the community. I've begun to talk to some non-profits who are considering designing recovery-related programs that incorporate exercise.

"Lastly, I really enjoy talking about recovery and addiction. I enjoy public speaking and practiced it a lot while I worked in the prison. For years, I've had people tell me that I should share my story and I'd like to find more ways to do that. I'd also like to get back to podcasting in the future because it allows me to be creative and share the ways I'm continuing to grow and learn. And when I feel creative, I feel more engaged with my life, which keeps me motivated. In brief, I hope to share the lessons I've learned through this program to help others struggling with addiction.

"As I mentioned, I've dealt with racing thoughts throughout my life, primarily focused on negative areas of my life. Coupled with the stressors that I created from young to middle adulthood, these racing thoughts made it difficult for me to sleep, further increasing my anxiety. In recovery, I've been able to better utilize these thoughts, and much of my recent academic success is the result of my having learned to focus on whatever task I need to accomplish next. I've now begun to take this focus and redirect it toward my desire to share my story and talk to people about recovery. In fact, these racing thoughts are currently focused on an idea I have for a book."

The End

(re)making a sandwich

AFTERWORD

I believe it is important to provide some transparency around the context of this book. I started out with the desire to tell my recovery story. When I began thinking about it, I was in a reasonably grounded place in my life. I had graduated with my master's in social work a few months prior and had been working as a counselor for almost four years. Having decided on my goal, I needed to determine how best to chronicle my recovery journey. I spent months contemplating different approaches: writing style options, such as which narrative point of view to use and how to choose tenses; and content issues, such as how much personal detail to reveal. These sorts of questions baffled me. At last, I did what I always do when I need to process something: I went for a run.

As I ran, it occurred to me that clinical documentation was a writing style I used daily, and a story written from the perspective of a counselor's notes might produce an entertaining read. And from this, the idea for the book was born.

From this writing perspective I could utilize my own assessment results and homework assignments to include some details of my personal life. As mentioned in the preface, Frank's story is a combination of fictional and non-fictional elements. I did complete drug and alcohol treatment and continue with individual counseling on my way to completing the DISP program; this much—and many of the other details of Frank's story—were borrowed from my own experiences. The characters in the groups, however, are fictional. Their stories, and their phrasing, take bits and pieces from group counseling and community support meetings I've attended over the years. They are examples of the stories and wisdom anyone might hear in a group recovery environment.

In telling Frank's story post-DISP I wanted to demonstrate that just because one completes a rehabilitation program doesn't mean that life stops presenting setbacks. People struggling with addiction may be at risk of relapse regardless of how many years they have abstained from a substance.

I created a fictional research study that allowed for a setting in which the Primary Counselor and Frank could continue to meet and talk about life. As anyone who has been through treatment or worked at a counseling agency knows, long-term treatment and post-treatment aftercare are not always options. The major events and feelings Frank describes in the book happened to me, with one significant exception: I did not continue to work with a counselor individually as Frank does in the story. This fiction includes the exit interview with the panel members at the end of the six years, which was a literary device used to allow me to summarize some of what I considered the most important aspects of the DISP program, and of my experiences in recovery in general.

This story is in many ways an addiction self-help book. There are countless useful sayings associated with addiction and recovery, many of which come from the literature of Alcoholics Anonymous. For example, "take what you need and leave the rest." For those embarking or already on a recovery journey: Not all that was shared in this book will be helpful with your addiction and recovery process. I hope you will take with you what you found helpful and leave the rest on the pages. People who struggle with addiction have significantly different trauma histories, risk/protective factors, mental health symptoms, and health concerns. These all contribute to different severities of substance use disorders. What can be utilized to treat and engage with one person may not be effective for another person, and conversely, one need not have a substance use disorder to find many of the principles present in this book useful in navigating through life. That being said, I would like to share some aspects of addiction and recovery that I believe to be universal truths.

A person without a disease like addiction is likely to have most body systems working in a relatively balanced, routine way. This is referred to as **homeostasis**. If there is a disturbance or disorder to this balance the body and mind will naturally try to establish order in an effort to return to homeostasis.

For someone struggling with addiction, however, the balanced order gets switched, so the person's 'normal' becomes when they are using the substance. This reverse order of balance is called **allostasis**. The person feels well when they are using and unwell when not, and the body will use withdrawal symptoms and cravings to drive the person to use again.

Recovery is the process of returning the body to its natural homeostasis from the destructive allostasis. This is not an overnight fix and requires that the body go through withdrawal and cravings to establish a period of sobriety. This can feel very overwhelming, especially as it generally occurs at the same time that people with addiction are confronted with the frequently significant and multifaceted tolls addiction has taken on their lives. The feelings accompanying the absence of the addictive chemical, combined with the recognition, by the person struggling with addiction, of the many practical problems addiction often leaves in its wake, may result in that person's returning to substance use as a way to numb these feelings. Accepting the inevitability of, and discomfort likely to accompany, these thoughts and feelings is an important part of recovery.

There are well constructed neural pathways in the brain that lead to the thoughts, emotions, and behaviors that contribute to the continued use of chemical substances. The process of building new neural pathways is a necessary step towards recovery. I like to think of them as trails; the new trail needs to be used often to become more established and easier to navigate. As the old trails that support the addiction are used less and less, they will become overgrown with weeds and more difficult to traverse. The new trails support healthy coping skills that better align with a person's values.

Other areas that are key to achieving/maintaining homeostasis may include spirituality, sleep, diet, exercise, mental health, motivation to continue abstinence, relationship repair, boundaries, financial repair, building a recovery support group, legal issues, parenting/childcare issues, employment, and education. Given all of this, it's understandable that recovery is such hard work and that a person may relapse again and again as they work to create new neural pathways. This is also why the AA slogan "One day at a time" is so profound in this context.

Empathy: For those reading this book who are not struggling with addiction, try to imagine what it is like to be devoted to a substance that is trying to kill you. This devotion to the substance and the behaviors that are needed to continue to use it tends to lead people with substance use disorders to feel powerlessness to change. People with addiction may understand that they need to change the cycle they are in but feel incapable of this on their own, and they will often experience anxiety and/or depression that comes from being in a state where they feel helpless to control their actions and feelings. In order to support someone struggling with addiction, we must be able to mentally place ourselves in that person's situation. This allows us to feel empathy rather than judgment.

I also want to acknowledge, however, how difficult it can be to refrain from judging someone struggling with addiction. The family members, friends, children, and partners of people with addiction often experience feelings of powerlessness and helplessness similar to those experienced by the people with addiction. Stress levels increase, causing problems like sleepless nights, anxiety, high blood pressure, and often relationship issues. Addiction is felt by everyone connected to the system of the person experiencing it, which is one of the reasons it is often referred to as a "family disease." The family unit often changes and adapts to the addiction as it becomes its own identity at the center of the family, much like the center spoke on a wagon wheel. Just as the person with addiction will not be able to heal on their own, the family system may also need support. Seeking support through Al-Anon, family support groups in worship-related settings, or individual and family therapy can help both the individual and the family heal and grow.

Openness: For many people who struggle with addiction, a rigid way of thinking has been hardwired in their brain chemistry and contributes to continued substance use. These folks speak in absolutes stating, "It will **always** be this way" or "I'd **never** be able to do that." The thinking keeps them stuck in the pattern of allostasis or needing a substance to help get through life. This rigid thinking works to isolate people from the positive and supportive aspects of their lives, as they are often unable to see a different perspective or unable to change their mind about a situation. The addiction has placed blinders on them so as not to distract from the irrational perceived truths that they are miserable, that there is nothing wrong, that nothing that can be done, and/or that they need substances to deal with life. To take a step towards recovery, the blinders must come off. The person must be able to see that all of life's moments have different perspectives and be open to this new way of thinking. Looking inward towards your values will provide a compass to move forward. Understanding the thinking and behaviors that lead you towards a value driven life has been the recovery foundation that I have followed. This can be done with or without spirituality. Many find spirituality and God in recovery because the perspective shift can lead to a belief that you are meant to struggle to have the opportunity to change. This connection to a higher power can be the catalyst to a seismic shift in the way a person interacts with their life and the world around them.

Recovery should be synonymous with growth. Closed thinking does not allow for continued self-improvement or challenging one's own beliefs. A powerful statement for growth is "maybe I don't know everything". Try saying it out loud and check in with yourself to see how you feel saying it. I hope that you carry that statement with you beyond the pages of this book, as an opportunity to be open to learning. This can have a tremendously positive impact on your life and those around you.

To conclude, in this book I describe how shame affected my life and how it intertwined with my depression and continued alcohol use. I want to clarify, however, that I am not a victim. Yes, I spent many years of my life feeling shame, but a great deal of this shame was a result of my behaviors and the chaos and destruction they caused in other people's lives. I chose not to go into detail about some of these behaviors in the book as I did not want to cause distress to people who experienced them and might find reading about them retraumatizing, but I also don't want to completely slant the narrative of the book in my favor. I have lied, cheated, stolen, fought, yelled, kept silent when I should have been talking, broken laws, and a host of other behaviors that do not align with my values. Although it is sometimes tempting to "defend" myself by pointing to some of the (even worse?) things I didn't do, it is incredibly important for me to acknowledge how abusive many of my actions were. I have made sexual advances without consent. I have made comments, jokes, and microaggressions about oppressed groups of people. I have also listened to others with privilege do the same without speaking up. None of this is ok.

Since being in recovery I have reached out to many people to make amends, as is the practice in most recovery programs. As noted above, a reminder of a bad experiences can be damaging in and of itself. Therefore, in amends work, one must be careful, when contemplating reaching out to someone with an amends, to avoid doing so if one thinks the other person might find it retraumatizing. In instances such as this, I work to make amends by how I choose to live my life today. I now make every effort to avoid causing anyone harm and I take responsibility when I do. I try to be of service to and help others. And most importantly, I am trying to raise boys to be men who do not follow the same destructive patterns.

Relatedly, I think it is important to remember that the words "I'm sorry" or "thank you," used without the appropriate actions, can easily be manipulation. If I use words in place of action to express gratitude or regret, they're meaningless. This book and my life of recovery are my efforts to show my intentions through actions.

ACKNOWLEDGEMENTS

Deacon-for being you, providing me with the motivation for everything I have done since you were born. For being my biggest cheerleader. You are my light.

Dana-for the laughs and jokes. For the love and support. For your resiliency. For letting me into your family. For letting me have every minute I got with you and Joseph.

Joseph-for the effortless humor. For the talent you continue to show. For being a wonderful example to Deacon. For getting to be in the front row to see how incredible of a young man you have become.

The Orr Family-for always being on my side, up or down.

Nancy and Jeannie, my editors from Guide On The Side-for the tireless work it took to sculpt what I gave you into this completed book. For being invested in this project. For the wonderful conversations around the material and life in general. For using soft words to make tough points.

Adrienne-for sacrificing your time to help shape the rawest rough draft into something that could be shown to other people. For seeing my writing flaws as just something to work on. For your friendship.

Samyuell Mongkhounsavath- for taking an author picture that somehow makes me seem professional.

Charles Patterson-for the help in designing the book cover and formatting assistance. Your insight was so needed and motivating to end this project.

Andy Meaden-for helping format this into something readable, if people get something from this it will be in large part because of how easy it was to read.

The American Society of Addiction Medicine-thanks for granting permission to use the ASAM criteria and model in my book, was truly helpful in the supporting the vision I had for this project.

And to all the folks out there doing this one day at a time, keep grinding, have some compassion towards yourself, and never forget it's not better back out there using!

NOTES

i   Fees

The program's fees can eliminate even motivated candidates who are economically disadvantaged. The cost of the alcohol monitoring bracelet, restitution and court costs and the monthly probation cost, while substantial, can be spread over the period of the program and do not carry the likely penalty of being sent to jail for missing a single payment. Costs reduce after the first 90 days and further after the first year.

Breakdown of program fees:

- $16 per day for alcohol monitoring bracelet (first ninety days)

- $40 per UDS; six–eight per month the first year, four per month the final two years

- $25 per weekly group counseling for the treatment year

- $40 per individual counseling session, twice per month for treatment year

- $15 monthly probation cost

- $5,000 for restitution and court costs; must be paid in full by the end of program

iii   Research Study Methodology

This transcription format is typical in thematic analysis in qualitative studies; i.e. those studies that are designed to find patterns among participants. For example, if six out of ten study participants report that the requirement of utilizing public transportation is stressful due to lack of funds available to pay the fare, this pattern could be used to infer that cost of fare could be problematic for study participants' success. As this is a case study of one participant, there will be no comparative analysis among participants.

iii Intake

When a substance use treatment provider is presented with a potential client, s/he needs to evaluate two basic areas. These two areas are screening and assessment.

- Screening simply determines the presence or absence of a substance use problem.
- Assessment classifies the specifics of the problem and suggests optimal treatment.

A drug and alcohol assessment is a tool utilized by substance abuse treatment providers to determine each client's treatment priorities and needs. It's used frequently in the insurance industry to determine the level of care necessary for a specific patient.

iv At the time of this assessment, the DSM-IV was the most current source of information regarding how to diagnose problems with substance use. To meet the criteria for an Alcohol Dependence diagnosis according to the DSM-IV, Frank would have had to answer 'yes' to three or more of the above questions; he answered 'yes' to all seven. The DSM-V update, published in 2013, modified some of the DSM-IV's diagnostic criteria. For instance, the use of the words, "dependence" and "abuse," which were part of the classification language in the DSM-IV, were changed to the single term "use disorders." The above questions are included in the DSM-V, as well as others that are used to evaluate clients' substance cravings, whether they use the substance in dangerous situations, and what impact their use has on family and friends.

There are 11 questions in the DSM-V that determine the severity level of the user's substance problems. The level of substance use disorder is determined by the number of questions to which a client answers 'yes.' A 'yes' to six or more questions establishes a disorder label of 'severe.' Four to five 'yes' responses dictate the label 'moderate,' and two to three the label 'mild.' If Frank had been diagnosed using the DSM-V criteria, he would have had a diagnosis of Severe Alcohol Use Disorder.

v Motivational Interviewing is a counseling method that seeks to help clients resolve ambivalent feelings and insecurities in an effort to activate the internal motivation they need to change their behavior.

Cognitive Behavioral Therapy (CBT) is a psychotherapeutic treatment that helps clients identify and change destructive thought patterns that negatively influence behaviors and emotions.

Narrative Therapy is a counseling approach that seeks to mentally separate clients from identifying with their problems by analyzing each client's narrative about his/her life experiences.

vi   Boersma, Peter, Maria A. Villarroel, and Anjel Vahratian. "Heavy Drinking Among U.S. Adults, 2018—Products - Data Briefs - Number 374- August 2020." Centers for Disease Control and Prevention. Centers for Disease Control and Prevention, August 18, 2020. https://www.cdc.gov/nchs/products/databriefs/db374.htm.

Made in the USA
Monee, IL
31 October 2021